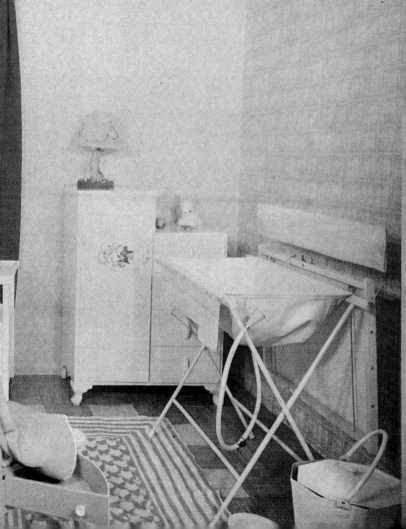

GOOD HOUSEKEEPING'S BABY BOOK

First published 1944
Reprinted 1944
Reprinted 1945
Reprinted 1945
Second edition 1946
Third edition 1947
Fourth edition 1948
Fifth edition 1948
Sixth edition 1949
Seventh edition 1950
Reprinted 1950
Eighth edition 1952
Reprinted 1952
Ninth edition 1953
Tenth (Revised) edition 1955
Reprinted 1956
Eleventh (Revised) edition 1957
Twelfth (Revised) edition 1959

Printed by Morrison & Gibb Ltd.
London and Edinburgh

GOOD HOUSEKEEPING'S

Baby Book

by

The Good Housekeeping
Family Doctor
in conjunction with
Good Housekeeping Family Centre

The National Magazine Company Ltd.
28–30 Grosvenor Gardens, London, S.W.1

Foreword

This twelfth revised edition of the Baby Book comes to you with the good wishes of the Good Housekeeping Family Doctor and of Mrs. Nora Aris of the Good Housekeeping Family Centre, who have combined to produce this much enlarged volume, containing authoritative information on all aspects of baby care during the first two years.

As Medical Officer in a busy Welfare Centre, the Doctor is in constant touch with the latest developments in medical science as they affect the well-being of mothers and their babies, and she offers expert advice on the health of the expectant mother, the birth of the baby, feeding and weaning, the treatment of minor ailments and so on. Mrs. Aris gives up-to-date information about the layette (including both knitted and sewn garments), nursery equipment, clothes for the expectant mother, baby routine and management and advice to parents who are considering adopting a baby.

The mother who is looking forward to the birth of her baby (particularly her first baby) is faced with many problems. It is our aim, through the pages of this Baby Book, to give practical and friendly advice on these problems in a way that will help to make the waiting time, as well as the first months after the baby's birth, a really happy period in a mother's life.

Contents

List of Plates

Happy hearts and happy faces,
Happy play in grassy places—
That was how, in ancient ages
Children grew to kings and sages.
ROBERT LOUIS STEVENSON

The First Baby

You think you are going to have a baby, and your mind is full of questions. First you want to have your hopes confirmed. Then you want to know how to prepare yourself for the birth of the baby, so that all may be normal and straightforward. There are arrangements for the confinement to be made, preparations for the baby to be thought out, clothes and equipment to be bought or made, and finally you want to know all you can about baby's management and feeding. We believe that the nine months of waiting for baby's arrival can be very happy and useful months, and that the first year of your child's life can lay the foundations of a happy future for you both. This book has been written to guide and help you through this busy and joyful period of your life.

The first arresting sign of pregnancy, in the woman who menstruates regularly, is the missing of a menstrual period, and when two periods have been missed it is fairly safe to assume that you are going to have a baby. Especially is this the case if the omission is accompanied by a slight enlargement of the breasts, which will also feel heavier and more sensitive. Other signs are the onset of a feeling of emptiness or nausea in the mornings, a desire to pass water more frequently, and a feeling of fatigue in the evenings.

The missing of a menstrual period is not a sure sign

in those who menstruate irregularly, and it may be necessary to have a medical examination before a true diagnosis can be made.

There are other tests which a doctor can make. By examination he can tell with certainty when the womb is the size of a three months' pregnancy, but by a special test of the urine the diagnosis can be made as early as a fortnight after the first missed period. It is wise to see your doctor as soon as you suspect you are pregnant.

The date of baby's expected arrival is calculated from the date of the beginning of your last period. Add seven days to this date and then add nine months. (See table below.) The date thus given is the approximate day on which baby will be born.

Date of first day of last menstrual period		Date of baby's expected arrival
January 10th		October 17th
March 18th	Add 7 days	December 25th
June 28th	and then add	April 5th
September 1st	nine months	June 8th
November 5th		August 12th

Ante-natal care

As soon as you know you are pregnant, you should make arrangements for your ante-natal care with your doctor or with the Ante-Natal Clinic at your Welfare Centre or at the hospital where you will have your baby. Regular medical supervision throughout your pregnancy is most necessary.

The address of your nearest Welfare Centre can be obtained by enquiring at your local Council offices, or by writing to the Medical Officer of Health for your area.

You are strongly advised to make all the arrangements in good time, so that you can take full advantage of available facilities. We give below, in broad outline, the arrangements now in force under the National Health Service and the National Insurance Act.

Responsibility for the Maternity and Child Welfare services is now concentrated in the local health authorities (County and County Borough Councils) in England and Wales. It is their function to provide maternity and child welfare clinics, midwives, health visitors, district nurses and domestic helps. They will also see that their services are closely integrated with the hospital service, and may make available the special equipment that is needed for premature babies.

At the Clinic : If you attend the Ante-Natal Clinic at the Welfare Centre, you will be seen by a midwife and a doctor. The midwife is, of course, specially qualified, and she may attend you when baby is born. The doctor, too, has had special experience in this work, and she will examine you thoroughly. After asking a few questions, the doctor will consider your general health, take your blood pressure, and examine your teeth, heart, lungs and a specimen of your urine. On this occasion or on a subsequent one she will take a little of your blood for testing.

Blood tests are done early in pregnancy, and possibly

again towards the end. They may reveal anæmia or other conditions which need to be treated. Your blood groups are determined, so that the right blood can be given without delay should a blood transfusion be necessary at any time, and so that preparations can be made to combat the possible effects of Rhesus incompatability. (See page 34.)

At the Clinic you should also have the opportunity of preparing yourself for your new job of motherhood. Some clinics hold mothercraft classes and give useful demonstrations and film shows illustrating different aspects of infant care. If there are sessions for learning relaxation and exercises to prepare you for the confinement, do take advantage of them.

Besides the expert advice which is given, the exchange of ideas between the mothers at the Clinic can be a real encouragement and help. The months before the baby is born are an ideal learning time, and if they are used fully, you will have so much more confidence, and will be so much happier, when you actually have the baby to care for yourself.

Ante-natal care by your own doctor : If you prefer, you can ask your own doctor to look after you during pregnancy and at the confinement. Your doctor will advise you, if necessary, about a nursing home, hospital or nurse, and will give you every help he can. In some cases he may not undertake maternity work under the National Health Service, and if this is so he will give you details of other doctors in the neighbourhood who are experienced in obstetrics.

Anæsthetics and pain-relieving drugs. When you first see your doctor, or visit the Clinic or maternity home, it would be wise to talk over the whole question of anæsthetics and pain-relieving drugs so that your mind may be at rest during your pregnancy.

If you think you will feel the need of a sedative or analgesic, it is nothing to be ashamed of to make sure beforehand that these will be there. Indeed, some of the classes for expectant mothers include instruction and practice in the use of the anæsthetic apparatus. Then, having every confidence in your attendant, you can do your best by co-operating in every way, both actively when you are asked, and passively by resting well between the contractions. The proper use of sedatives and analgesics should not affect the child in any way, and may greatly help the mother.

However, many mothers, having learnt to co-operate and relax sufficiently, prefer to be fully conscious during their baby's birth and have no need for these helps. If you wish to know more about what are called " natural childbirth " methods, information can be obtained from the Natural Childbirth Trust, 44 Great Russell Street, London, W.C.1. (Postal enquiries only.)

Dental care : During pregnancy and for a year after confinement, a mother can obtain all dental treatment free under the National Health Service. Under the local Health Authority Dental Service, any dentures needed would also be free, but if she goes to her own dentist under the National Health Service, although the treatment would be free, dentures would cost up to £4. 5s.

Hospital confinements

Hospital accommodation is available for mothers in cases of medical complication, and priority is given where home conditions are unsuitable and for first babies. Application for hospital admittance is normally made through your doctor. Where admission is required because of unsuitable home conditions, it may be made, through the Medical Officer of Health, by the doctor at the Ante-Natal Clinic. The service is free.

Where single rooms are a medical necessity, they are made available without charge.

In some hospitals patients may obtain more privacy (under the National Health Service) by booking an "amenity" bed in a small ward or single room, when available. There is a minimum charge for such accommodation, but the services in an amenity bed and the doctor's attendance are free, as in the general ward.

In many hospitals there are also special private rooms available for private patients who choose to pay both the full cost and all medical and surgical fees.

Nursing homes

If you prefer to go privately to a paying nursing home, your doctor will probably advise you on the choice of a suitable one. Here again it is essential to book up early, and it is a good plan to have a chat with the matron some time before you go in, when you can also see what accommodation is available and make full enquiries into the fees and "extras."

Home confinements

There are two main methods of arranging these.

(a) By engaging the free services of a midwife and/or doctor under the National Health Service Act, as already mentioned. Your own family doctor, the local midwife or the Ante-Natal Clinic will help you make all necessary arrangements, and will put you in touch with any other services you may need. In all cases the midwife will help with advice about the arrangement of the bedroom for the confinement and preparations for baby's coming, and she (with your doctor or the Clinic doctor) will give full ante-natal care. After the confinement, the midwife will continue to visit daily during the lying-in period, and will give you every nursing care ; for the first few days she will also visit you in the evening. When the midwife ceases her visits, the health visitor will call and give any advice needed.

(b) By arranging with the doctor who attends you as a private paying patient (or with a specialist recommended by him) to attend you, and by engaging a resident or visiting maternity nurse (or midwife) privately. Your own doctor will advise about getting in touch with a maternity nurse. (If you have booked a doctor for your maternity care under the Health Service Act, but want to engage a resident maternity nurse, your doctor will advise you how to get one.)

It is customary to book a resident nurse for four weeks, though you may be able to get one for three weeks only. If you feel you cannot afford to keep the maternity nurse for the full period, do at least try to arrange for some domestic assistance, a Home Help (see below) or a friend to come for the first week or two after she leaves. Although mothers are now encouraged to get up for short periods from the first week, many make the mistake of getting back to their full domestic round too quickly, and risk losing their breast milk in consequence.

Get to know the maternity nurse as well as you can beforehand—if she visits you when you first book her up, she will be able to give you much valuable advice and help on the equipment, etc.

If you are having your baby at home and really need someone to take over your household duties, you should enquire from the Public Health Department of your local Council Offices about the Home Helps scheme. In some districts it may not be easy to provide adequate domestic help, but in others the scheme is working well. A Home Help can take over your domestic duties during the day-time, but will not be resident. You would be expected to pay according to your means towards the cost of the help.

Should you need resident help during the lying-in period, and you have no relative or friend who could stay with you, then the best plan is to make local enquiries by asking your neighbours or by advertising.

Milk and welfare foods

You are entitled to reduced-price milk and vitamin supplements, and to obtain them this is the procedure :

Take or send your Certificate of Pregnancy to the local office of the Ministry of Pensions and National Insurance, and you will receive in exchange a Milk Token Book (EM). The tokens in it will entitle you to 7 pints of liquid milk a week, at 4d. a pint. You will also receive a card of tokens entitling you to a bottle of concentrated orange juice for 5d. every 9 days. Other coupons enable you to have a free packet of vitamin A and D tablets every 6 weeks, or, if you prefer, you can have cod liver oil. These can all be obtained at any Welfare Foods Distribution Centre. (Your Welfare Clinic or the local Public Health Department will give you the address.) See that you renew your Milk Token Book as necessary.

The maternity benefits

Under the National Insurance Scheme, the present maternity grant is £12. 10s., which may be paid on either the mother's own insurance or her husband's. The husband or wife on whose insurance the grant is being claimed must have paid at least twenty-six contributions of any class between becoming insured and the date or expected date of the confinement, and have paid or been credited with at least twenty-six contributions of any class in the last contribution year before the benefit year in which the confinement takes place or is expected. The maternity grant can be claimed as early as nine weeks before the week in which the confinement is expected, but not later than three months after it.

A home confinement grant of £5 is paid if the baby is born at home or elsewhere not at the public expense. A home confinement grant can only be paid if a maternity grant has been awarded. This is claimed after the confinement, but not later than three months after it.

A maternity allowance of 50s. a week, usually for eighteen weeks, starting eleven weeks before the expected week of confinement, is paid to mothers who are normally employed or self-employed and who pay full national insurance contributions. It is a condition that the mother does no work besides her own domestic duties while she is drawing the maternity allowance. She can claim it fourteen weeks before the expected week of confinement.

Claim forms and explanatory leaflets can be obtained from a Ministry of National Insurance local office.

The Health of the Expectant Mother

The time of waiting and preparing for the baby should be a full and happy one, both for the expectant mother and for her husband. The miracle of the baby's growth should be a source of wonder to you both, drawing you closer in a new bond.

In the beginning, there are, of course, adjustments to be made. Some women find they are more emotional and more easily upset, and they feel anxious about new experiences and responsibilities to come. Such an attitude is quite natural and should be dealt with sensibly, but having made arrangements for your ante-natal care and your confinement you should have confidence in your doctor, Clinic or midwife. Learn all you can about mothercraft, and follow the health rules given here.

This is the time when the husband's support can be of the greatest help to the expectant mother. Taking care not to over-tire yourself, you should make the most of these months to go out together, perhaps to enjoy a carefree holiday, to enjoy yourselves as a couple. Your husband's strength and understanding should be at your disposal if you feel a little emotional or worried, and you will need his affection to maintain your confidence in yourself as your figure becomes heavier.

There is equipment to be chosen, probably a nursery to furnish, and in all these practical plans your husband will want to take an active share. If you work together in planning for the baby, the ground will be prepared for sharing his care when he is born.

It will help you to bring an intelligent understanding to your pregnancy if you know something of the bodily processes which are taking place. First it will be necessary to explain a few technical terms, so that you will be able to understand the description in the paragraphs below.

The womb is the muscular framework in which the baby lies—its other name is the uterus. This expands as baby grows, and the muscle walls become thicker and richer in blood. It is lined with a membrane, which also becomes very much thickened and thrown up into folds. The fertilised egg cell (or ovum) embeds itself in the membrane, which at that point becomes specially thick and sends out processes into the muscle of the uterus, forming the after-birth or placenta.

Elsewhere the membrane remains thinner, and with the covering formed by the growing foetus, forms the bag of membranes. At the end of the third month the foetus and its membranes have entirely filled the cavity of the uterus, so there is never any bleeding unless things are abnormal.

From the centre of the placenta a cord runs to the navel or umbilicus of the baby, and in this cord are arteries and a vein. The vein carries the mother's blood to the baby ; from this blood it gets all its nourishment, and the arteries return the blood (now carrying waste products) back to the mother, the placenta acting as a filter.

All round the baby, inside the bag of membranes and

placenta, are the "waters," or amniotic fluid. This fluid acts as a shock-absorber, protecting baby from any minor bumps, and also allows him some movement.

The womb communicates with the exterior by means of a canal running through the neck of the womb, which is called the cervix ; this projects into the vagina.

All these changes and growth naturally bring about a change in your weight, and it has been found that the normal gain in weight during pregnancy may be as much as 24 pounds.

At first, baby is very tiny and can only be seen with the aid of a lens, but at the end of three months he is just over three inches in length, and is perfectly formed in nearly every detail.

You should begin to feel baby's movements some time during the fifth month of pregnancy. At first these are very slight and difficult to distinguish from wind. They really feel like tiny flutterings, but if you are on the watch you will soon recognise them.

As baby grows you will be astonished at the strength of his movements. He kicks with his legs, moves his arms, and sometimes swings his whole body round. Usually he lies head downwards, with buttocks uppermost. As his legs are bent up, his buttocks are very prominent, and often to the inexperienced hand they feel like the head, and the mother worries unnecessarily, thinking that baby is lying the wrong way up.

If baby's movements keep you awake at night, it will help you to sleep on your side and put a small pillow under the abdomen. The womb enlarges gradually as baby grows, its height reaching the navel at the sixth month, and during the ninth month it reaches as far as the lower border of the ribs. Two or three weeks before baby is due to be born, he begins to drop right into the pelvic cavity ; when the womb sinks in this way the mother feels lighter, and breathing is easier.

General health rules

The changes which are taking place in your body are a normal process, and what is required from you is to adopt common-sense rules and to follow a healthful routine. Diet and exercise, two very important factors in good health, are dealt with in detail in this chapter.

Your teeth should receive special attention and you should have them examined early in the pregnancy. (See page 11.)

Take warm, not hot, baths regularly, especially during the last three months. Make sure that your bowels act freely : suggestions for dealing with constipation are given on pages 35–36.

Above all, remember that a calm, unworried attitude of mind is one of the best allies of good health.

Diet in pregnancy

There is no need to eat very largely during pregnancy. You may find that you feel uncomfortably full if you stick to the usual three large meals a day, and it may suit you better to have small meals more frequently. You will just have to experiment and find out what is best for you. Keep to a good all-round diet, including as much vegetables, fruit, milk, cheese, meat, fish and eggs in your menu as possible. They will help you to nourish the baby properly, and will not be fattening for you.

Fish is a very useful food, for it contains body-building protein, iodine and some of the essential fats, and it is easily used by the body. Do not despise the herring, as this is really one of the most nourishing of the fish family. If you like liver, you should have it lightly fried or cooked in a casserole once a week.

At the moment the Welfare Food Service allows you a pint of milk a day at a reduced price, but take more if you can, because it is a good source of the essential mineral calcium, which builds teeth and bone. Take the milk in any way you fancy—in puddings and soups, with cereals, or as a drink flavoured with tea, coffee or yeast extract, for instance. You are also allowed orange juice and cod liver oil or vitamin A and D tablets, and these extras supply you with vitamins which are vitally important (see pages 14–15).

To help you plan your diet, we give in the following pages suggested menus for a week.

Sunday

BREAKFAST	DINNER
Cereal and milk	Roast meat
Boiled egg	Greens and potatoes
Toast, butter, etc.	Stewed fruit and
Coffee or tea	custard sauce

(Sunday continued)

TEA	SUPPER
Tomato or watercress sandwiches	Cheese pudding or cheese and biscuits
Cake Tea	Fruit juice

Monday

BREAKFAST	DINNER
Grapefruit	Cold meat salad
Cereal and milk	Baked potato in jacket
Toast, butter and honey	Bread and butter
Coffee or tea	pudding

TEA	SUPPER
Marmite sandwiches	Scrambled egg, toast
Cake or biscuit	Cheese and biscuits
Tea	Fruit juice

Tuesday

BREAKFAST	DINNER
Bacon and tomato	Macaroni cheese
Toast, butter, etc.	Vegetables
Coffee or tea	Sponge pudding
Orange	

TEA	SUPPER
Bread and butter	Egg or sardine salad
Honey or jam	Bread and butter
Cake or biscuit	Milky coffee or
Tea	other drink

Wednesday

BREAKFAST	DINNER
Grapefruit	Liver
Boiled egg	Vegetables
Toast, butter and honey	Fruit fool
Coffee or tea	

TEA	SUPPER
Cheese sandwiches	Vegetable soup
Cake or biscuit	Bread or toast
Tea	Horlicks

Thursday

BREAKFAST	DINNER
Stewed fruit and cereal	Stewed meat and
Toast, butter and	vegetables
marmalade	Pancakes with lemon
Coffee or tea	and sugar

TEA	SUPPER
Tomato or watercress	Cold ham or other cold
sandwiches	meat and salad
Cake or biscuits	Bread and butter
Tea	Milk

Friday

BREAKFAST	DINNER
Scrambled or poached egg	Steamed fish and
Toast, butter and honey	white sauce
Coffee or tea	Vegetables
Raw apple or other fruit	Jam tart and custard

(Friday continued)

TEA

Marmite sandwiches
Bread and butter
Tea

SUPPER

Savoury omelette
Milk

Saturday

BREAKFAST

Cereal and milk
Grapefruit or other fruit
Toast and marmalade
Coffee or tea

DINNER

Bacon and tomato
Vegetables
Queen of puddings

TEA

Egg sandwiches
Cake or biscuits
Tea

SUPPER

Grilled herring
Bread and butter
Coffee

Reminders

1. Remember that these menus are meant only as a guide and can be varied as desired.

2. Whenever possible have some fresh raw vegetables and fruit each day. Watercress, raw shredded cabbage or Brussels sprouts, parsley, tomatoes, raw carrot, and the summer fruits (especially blackcurrants) are all good sources of vitamins. The Bramley Seedling is the only variety of apple with appreciable vitamin content.

3. Cooked vegetables are also good, provided that they are boiled quickly without bicarbonate of soda, and in a small amount of water (which can be used for soup).

4. There is no virtue in drinking more water than

you feel you need. Indeed, if you have a tendency to puffy ankles, your doctor may suggest reducing fluids.

5. Remember your orange juice or fresh oranges and cod liver oil or vitamin capsules really are important.

6. If you have a tendency to over-weight neither you nor the baby will lose any nourishment if you omit all pastry, fried food, chocolate, sweets, puddings, cream, biscuits, buns, cakes, cocoa and other similar beverages from your diet. Starch-reduced rolls are less fattening than bread. Take your milk skimmed—it is still rich in protein and calcium. Any marked increase in weight should be immediately reported to your doctor.

Diet and the size of the baby : Diet has its main effect upon the health of the expectant mother. It has been proved again and again that the child takes the nourishment it needs, whatever the diet of the mother, so that unless the mother is well fed, she will become undernourished during her pregnancy, and may even suffer some deficiency. If this stage is reached the developing baby may suffer. There is no evidence that eating less will cause the child to be smaller in size.

Smoking : Some authorities say that " no smoking " is the rule during pregnancy and breast-feeding, but others have experimented, and as a result it can be said that moderate smoking has no harmful effect on the baby. A limit of seven cigarettes a day is a useful working rule, and if you find it impossible to cut down to this number it is best to give up smoking altogether.

Alcohol : An occasional glass of wine is harmless, but avoid the daily cocktail habit, and spirits generally.

Exercise for the expectant mother

Make it a rule to have a good walk every day. Ordinary housework will also help you greatly and give you quite satisfactory exercise, but avoid all movements requiring sudden or prolonged effort, such as is involved in lifting heavy weights, turning a mattress, or stretching up to a high shelf.

Unless you have previously had a miscarriage, or suggestive signs of one (see page 34), there is no reason why you should not continue, for as long as you comfortably can, cycling and short games of golf and tennis to which you are accustomed. The golden rule about exercise, and all exertion during pregnancy, is " Stop when you feel at all tired."

Ante-natal exercises and relaxation

(Illustrated on Plate IX)

The value of exercises and of the practice of relaxation in the preparation for childbirth is being increasingly recognised. Many hospitals and Ante-natal Clinics are now running classes for expectant mothers, with excellent results. If you are fortunate enough to have any in your area, you are strongly advised to join ; otherwise the following suggestions will be found helpful in strengthening muscles, stretching ligaments and loosening the pelvic joints, in order to make the labour as easy as possible. Before starting these exercises, mention your intention to your doctor, in case it may be necessary to modify them at all for you. Practise them at odd times during the day ; it is better to do a few at a time and do them often, than to do them all once a day. Do all the suggested exercises smoothly and rhythmically, avoiding jerkiness, and finish with a short period of relaxation. Suitable music helps the sense of rhythm and gives added zest.

1. Lie on your back on bed or couch with the feet and legs supported on a cushion or pouffe. Bend the right foot forward and back from the ankle, and repeat with the left. Do this five times. Raise each leg in turn to a position at right angles to the body, hold for a moment, and lower slowly. After a few weeks it may be possible to raise both together.

2. Stand with feet astride and lift your arms so that your finger-tips touch across your chest and your elbows are level with your shoulders. Fling the arms outwards and then bring them back to the first position. Repeat five times.

3. Sit on a low chair or stool and raise both arms sideways to shoulder height. Turn the palms up, breathing in through the nose. Now lower the arms to the side, while breathing out. Repeat this exercise five times.

4. Sitting as in Exercise 3, twist the trunk to the right as far as you can without moving the chair. Repeat to the left, and then to the right, and continue alternately up to four times, twisting evenly and rhythmically and without holding the breath.

5. Lie on bed or floor with knees bent and the soles of the feet resting flat on the bed or floor near the body. With arms relaxed at sides, breathe in, pushing out both

the ribs and the abdomen. Repeat five times, easily and rhythmically.

6. Get down on hands and knees, raise the back and tuck the buttocks and head in, then hollow the back and raise the head. Repeat five times slowly, and then fold the arms and rest the head on them, with the buttocks held high. If this exercise is done three or four times during the day, it will relieve the pressure upon the pelvic organs, and it is especially good for those with a tendency to hæmorrhoids or varicose veins of the vulva.

7. Stand with feet slightly apart, facing a support. Grasp the support and stand on tip-toe, then lower body into the squatting position, with knees held as wide apart as possible. Bounce up and down on the heels several times, and return to a standing position. (Not illustrated.)

The art of relaxation

Regular daily relaxation practice will lead to a lessening of tension, both physical and emotional, by reducing muscle-tone, and will help you to conserve your nervous energy ready for the demands which may be made upon it during confinement and afterwards. You will need, first of all, willingness to learn, and also definite instruction in the art, in order to practise it successfully. You will then be better able to relax during the labour itself, and thus to ensure the maximum dilatation of the birth passages, with the least possible discomfort.

Contrive to have at least half an hour during the day to practise relaxing. If there are no classes in your area the following suggestions will guide you :

Lie on your bed with your head comfortably supported

by a low pillow, with all your limbs in an easy position. Take a deep breath, very slowly pushing out your lower ribs and widening your back as you do so. Then let it out slowly and completely, feeling meanwhile that you are sinking through the bed. Fill your mind with pleasant, dreamy thoughts—for instance, about past restful holidays, day-dreams about your baby, or idle days in the sunlit country-side. Take another deep breath, and again " let go," as before. Now continue the process of relaxation by thinking of each part of the body in turn. Feel that your shoulders are opening outwards ; your arms falling from their sockets, quite limp ; your legs falling outwards by their own weight ; your back sinking through the bed ; your head falling backwards into the pillow by its own weight ; and, lastly, your face should be quite loose, with jaw relaxed and eyelids drooping. It is helpful to get someone else, preferably your husband, to give you these instructions at first, until you can memorise the routine.

The half-hour of relaxation every day should give you the necessary opportunity for rest. Unless you are ill, plenty of mild exercise is beneficial in every way, though you should take care not to become over-tired. Have at least eight hours in bed every night.

The expectant mother with a job

It is, of course, necessary to find out whether your employers have any objection to your continuing at work when you are pregnant. If this should be so—and it is becoming more rare—you should plan to discontinue work when pregnancy becomes obvious, which is usually some time before the end of the fifth month.

Otherwise, there is no reason why you should not continue to work until about eleven weeks before the baby is due, provided your work does not involve too much physical activity or standing. With a mind well occupied and hands kept busy, there is little time for worrying about minor aches and pains or food-fads. The chief disadvantage is that there is little possibility of the midday rest period, which is such a help in preparing for the confinement by learning relaxation of body and quietness of spirit, besides helping to prevent varicose veins and other complaints arising from pressure.

The demands of breast-feeding usually mean that return to work must be delayed for some six to eight months after baby's birth ; but if circumstances should necessitate bottle-feeding and a return to work, you should not think of going back for at least seven weeks. The mechanism of the body needs at least that time to return to normal, and eight weeks is really far better.

Preparation for breast-feeding

When you first attend the Ante-natal Clinic, or when your doctor examines you, the breasts and nipples will be inspected. If you know that one (or both) of your nipples is flat or pulled in, do not hesitate to point this out. If either of these conditions is present, the nipples will probably right themselves during the normal pregnancy development, but here are two helpful procedures :

(*a*) Take hold of the coloured area round the nipple and try to draw it out. If you succeed, wash and dry with a rough towel.

(*b*) If you cannot manage to draw out the nipple, it is often useful to wear plastic or glass nipple shields inside the brassière. They have a hole in the centre of one side which is placed over the nipple area, and the pressure of the rest of the shield over the surrounding area of breast helps to force the nipple out.

If the breasts and nipples are normal, it is not necessary to begin to prepare the nipples until the eighth month of pregnancy. Do not apply any Vaseline, glycerine or spirits to the nipples unless your nurse or doctor specially advises it ; usually it is quite sufficient if the nipple is gently drawn forward, so that it stands out well, and then washed and dried with a rough towel. Try to remove any crusts which may have formed on the nipple ; if necessary, apply fomentations two or three times to soften them, but never pull them off forcibly. These crusts are, of course, the dried secretion from the breasts which is the forerunner of the milk. Towards the end of the pregnancy it begins to ooze out from the many tiny openings on the nipple. It is a good plan during the last few weeks to learn to express just a few drops each day, in order to ensure that these ducts are not blocked. If the left breast is being expressed, use the right hand, placing the forefinger under the nipple and pointing towards the arm. Place the ball of the thumb just above the nipple, and gently but firmly and deeply close finger and thumb, squeezing out the secretion.

All through the pregnancy the breasts should be well supported, otherwise they will sag, the skin will stretch beyond recovery, and the figure will be lost.

Marital relationships during pregnancy

There is no reason to discontinue sexual intercourse during pregnancy ; indeed, husbands and wives will often feel a more intense desire than ever so to express their love for each other, because of their shared joy in their forthcoming parenthood. It is wise, however, to avoid the days when you would normally have been menstruating in the first three months of pregnancy, for this is the time when miscarriages are most likely to commence. If there is any previous history of a miscarriage, or a threatened miscarriage, it is best to abstain altogether until the fourth month is well over. The other time to avoid intercourse is during the last six weeks of the pregnancy, for there is then a slight risk of introducing infection.

Effect of illnesses during pregnancy

Many women are troubled about the possible effect on their baby of any illness during their pregnancy. Probably, however, there is only one disease about which they need be careful, and that is German measles. Although it is relatively mild in itself, it may sometimes adversely affect the baby, especially if the infection is caught in the early months of pregnancy, so take special care to avoid infection. If you do happen to come into contact with a case, see your doctor immediately, because, if it is available, he may want to give you an injection of Gamma Globulin, which will prevent you catching the infection.

Tendency to miscarriages

Most expectant mothers go through their pregnancy without any signs or thoughts of a miscarriage, but even the most normal of women should take simple precautions to avoid one, such as not carrying any heavy weight. There is nearly always someone else who can get in the coals for you, but if not, they will have to be carried in small amounts and not in heavy scuttles ! Another action to avoid is energetic stretching upwards, such as pushing up a heavy window, stretching up to reach something placed on a high shelf, etc.

If you have already had a miscarriage, or have been threatened with one, you will need to take special precautions until the end of the fourth month. First, and by far the most important, is adequate rest—breakfast in bed each day, and at least two hours' rest every afternoon, preferably lying on your tummy. Plan your day to fit in with this, and do not worry if the house is not cleaned as thoroughly as you would like. That can always be done later. Also avoid long bus rides.

Do not let yourself get constipated, but avoid anything except the mildest of purgatives ; liquid paraffin or Senokot are the best preparations to take. Avoid any sexual intercourse during these early months.

B.B.—3

Modern medical research can help you greatly if you have a tendency to miscarry. So do not hesitate to consult your doctor, if you know you have such a tendency, as early as possible in the new pregnancy.

Signs of a threatened miscarriage : Pain similar to a period pain which keeps recurring, or backache, and the loss of blood from the front passage (or vagina). If you suspect you have these symptoms, and certainly if you see a loss of blood, go to bed at once, where you should relax completely ; send for the doctor.

The Rhesus Factor

Of recent times there has been much unnecessary alarm about this question. Briefly, the position is this : If a wife with Rhesus-negative blood and a husband who has Rhesus-positive blood have a Rhesus-positive baby, there is a one in twenty chance that some of the baby's red blood corpuscles may be destroyed before birth, causing a variable degree of anæmia and jaundice when he is born. This almost never happens to the first baby in the family. But even if the baby is affected in this way, the condition may be so slight that it clears up completely with no treatment other than perhaps a little iron. If it is more severe, it may be necessary to exchange his blood for new by a special transfusion very soon after birth, and he will probably recover completely, with no subsequent ill-effects. It is only in very rare instances that the baby is still-born or his brain is permanently damaged. It can generally be foretold whether or not the baby is going to be affected by special blood tests on the mother, which reveal the presence of anti-bodies. If these are present in any quantity, the necessary preparations for giving a blood exchange to the baby soon after birth can be made, in case they are required. If the baby is affected by the Rhesus incompatibility of his parents, the signs are anæmia and jaundice which are present at birth or a few hours after. The jaundice which develops a day or two after birth is harmless, and has nothing to do with the Rhesus blood groups.

Common disorders in pregnancy

Given the right diet, enough exercise and a minimum of worry, there is no reason why you should not go all through your pregnancy in the best of health. Do not be disturbed if emotionally you are not quite as stable as usual. You may find that you easily alternate between states of happiness and depression. Other women may find that they tend to vegetate during pregnancy. As their body is actively creating, their mental capacities are not so active, and they find it difficult to concentrate on intellectual study—such matters as nappies and cot blankets will keep intruding.

The common disorders of pregnancy really fall into two divisions : those due to digestive difficulties, and those which are due to the mother's overburdened circulation.

Digestive difficulties include such things as :
Constipation : This usually occurs at some time or

another during pregnancy. It is wise to try to keep a
regular daily action, although an action on alternate days
may be more normal to you at this time. If the motion
is soft, there is no reason to take purgatives in order to
have a daily action, so long as you get a good and easy
evacuation on alternate days.

Plenty of water and as much fruit and greenstuff as
possible, combined with wholemeal bread or bran cereals,
and your daily orange juice should keep you regular.

The squatting position for defecation is the natural
and most helpful one for adequate elimination. At the
same time, it prepares the pelvis for an easy labour.

If you have to take a purgative, liquid paraffin taken
in any dose from 2 teaspoonfuls to 2 tablespoonfuls is
the best lubricant, and often all that is necessary. The
senna group of purgatives is also useful ; Senokot is a
reliable and effective senna preparation. During pregnancy avoid all drastic purgatives ; never take any aloes,
as these might irritate the muscle wall of the uterus.

A little gentle massage of the abdomen often helps the
static bowel. Begin low down over the appendix area,
on the right, and work round to the left, kneading the
walls and letting your fingers dig in deeply. This is very
useful, too, after baby is born, but consult your doctor
before you undertake the massage yourself.

Morning sickness : If you happen to suffer from this
complaint, it is a wise plan to have small, dry meals
fairly frequently during the day, starting with a dry
biscuit before you get out of bed. (Remember to get
up slowly.) Take your drinks between meals ; especially

is this wise if the sickness is present on occasion during the day. Extra sugar in drinks and on cereals helps some women, and is well worth trying. Many women taking Senokot for constipation also find it relieves nausea.

Ordinary morning sickness seldom lasts longer than the first three months of pregnancy, and half the battle is won if you decide to put up with it cheerfully and not to worry about it. But your doctor will be able to help you if the sickness becomes really bad.

Heartburn : This complaint very often troubles the expectant mother during the last three months of pregnancy. It is probably due to the fact that as the child grows, there is less room for the stomach to expand during and after meals. It usually helps to have frequent small meals, and to drink only between them, so that the stomach is not over-loaded. But if the symptom still occurs, an antacid tablet to suck often relieves it.

And now we come to consider those disorders and discomforts due to an overburdened circulation :

Varicose veins : Many expectant mothers complain of some degree of varicose veins either in the legs or in the vulva area. Several precautions can be taken to prevent the initial swelling of the veins—and the most important is rest. Try to get a rest every day, with the legs up, as already advised ; keep the feet raised higher than your seat when sitting during the day ; and get used to doing as many household chores as possible when sitting or propped against a high stool. A good support for the abdomen in the form of a maternity belt helps to take the weight off the legs. Do avoid wearing garters, because they tend to increase the congestion in the veins. If you do notice any swollen veins, the wearing of elastic stockings will prevent them from getting worse ; put them on in the mornings, with your legs elevated, before you get out of bed. Quite attractive elastic net ones are now on the market, and are cooler and more comfortable to wear than the old thicker kind.

Piles : These are really varicose veins, and the treatment is similar in some respects, especially so far as rest is concerned. If you notice any pain or swelling at the back passage, take extra care that your motions are not constipated, and that you have plenty of rest lying down. Liquid paraffin will help to keep the motions soft. It is particularly important for you to do exercise No. 6 on page 28.

There are some minor disorders of pregnancy which do not fall into the groups already covered ; these are due mainly to chemical changes in the mother's body.

Decaying teeth : During pregnancy it is wise to have the teeth overhauled at three-monthly intervals. There may be some calcium lack during these months, as baby is using the calcium in your bloodstream to form his bones and teeth. Remember that milk and cheese are the best sources of calcium, and your " expectant mother's supply " of Vitamins A and D helps in the absorption of the calcium. There are some preparations of calcium in which Vitamin D is included, but it is usually sufficient to take ordinary calcium-rich foods, provided you are careful also to take the extra vitamins available to you.

Cramp : This may also be caused by lack of calcium,

and is treated by taking extra rest and extra calcium. Do not think the tablet-form calcium is going to take the place of that contained in milk, cheese and vegetables. Take as much fresh greenstuff as you possibly can, and be sure to use the water in which the vegetables have been boiled to make either soups or gravy : this water contains much that is of value to the body. Sometimes extra salt in your food will cure pregnancy cramp.

Insomnia during the last two or three months of pregnancy is often present in a mild form. If it becomes at all marked, there is no reason why a sedative should not be taken, on your doctor's advice. A cup of thickened milk food taken before going to bed, and adequate rest during the day so that you do not become over-tired, will help you greatly.

Frequency of micturition : This can hardly be called a complaint, but you may find that you have to pass water much more frequently during pregnancy than you do normally. In fact, this is one of the early signs of pregnancy. It is due to the fact that the enlarged womb exerts pressure on the bladder during the second and third months. You will probably find that it will pass off after the third month, when the womb rises into the abdomen, and may return during the last weeks, when the head of the baby may press against the bladder. If this frequency bothers you, do not be tempted to limit your fluid intake too much, but, to avoid disturbed nights, there is no harm in restricting it during the evening. If, however, you should suffer any pain on passing water, tell your doctor.

Pregnancy cravings : Strong longings for certain foods, and for the taste or smell of inedible substances, are felt by many pregnant women. Others dislike foods and drinks previously enjoyed, such as bacon, tea and coffee, or hate the smell of tobacco until after the baby is born. Various explanations have been advanced—these likes and dislikes may point to a physiological need, be a way of combating nausea, or show emotional conflict. But no one really knows !

Danger signals

Lastly, there are a few signs which may point to conditions needing treatment. If any one of them is present, consult your doctor or midwife. They are :

1. Persistent vomiting after the third month of pregnancy.

2. Puffiness of the hands and ankles.

3. Severe and persistent headache.

4. Loss of blood from the front passage, or vagina, after the third month has been passed.

5. Marked increase in weight.

Do not be alarmed by this list of possible disorders that may beset you while you are carrying your baby. They must all be mentioned here if this book is to be of the greatest possible value to all expectant mothers, but in actual fact the great majority of women get through the nine months with surprising ease and well-being. In fact, many women feel better during pregnancy than at any other time in their lives.

Clothes and Looks

The clothes you wear when you are expecting a baby will make a good deal of difference to your poise and self-confidence ; provided you give some thought to the principles you should follow in your dress, you can look as attractive as ever. Many women feel particularly well during pregnancy, and their sense of personal fulfilment gives their faces a deeper beauty than it ever had before.

You will be well rewarded if you devote careful thought (though not necessarily very much money) to your wardrobe for your pregnancy. Of course there are problems—there is no need to pretend otherwise—but you can deal with them happily if you exercise good sense and imagination. The time for which you are planning is not long, but it does have very special requirements, so you should make sure that the clothes you choose will serve you well and give you the best possible value in comfort and smartness while you need them.

The first thing you have to consider is the time of year at which your baby is expected. The mother of a spring baby will need maternity clothes all through the winter months, and will have quite a lot of wear from them. It is not quite so easy for the mother of a summer or a winter baby, who will need special clothes for both warm and cold weather, so that she will probably have to compromise.

From four months

This is about the time when you begin to find that your skirts are becoming rather uncomfortably tight. But it is still too soon to change entirely to maternity wear, and it should be possible during this rather awkward stage to adapt your ordinary clothes. Skirts can be put on to looser waist-bands, or you might like to invest in a wrap-round skirt such as the " Estrava Adapta," which though it is not designed specially for maternity wear, has a four-inch expansion. A loose-fitting short jacket or top-coat is a most useful addition to your wardrobe.

In these early months, when your figure is just beginning to change, a pinafore frock made with a full skirt is easy to wear and has the great advantage of allowing for a variety of blouses or sweaters.

If you feel comfortable in slacks with a tunic, you would find them very practical to wear about the house during the middle months of your pregnancy. Slacks specially made for maternity wear can be bought or made from a pattern ; they are particularly useful if you attend classes for ante-natal exercises.

It is usual to have some fullness of the breasts from the early days of pregnancy, so you will need a brassière in a size larger than you normally wear. As the breasts have practically no muscle, it is essential for them to be well supported if you are to keep a good figure. No doubt you already know which make of brassière best suits your particular figure, and you will probably find that this firm makes a model specially for maternity wear. The ideal is that it should have broad shoulder straps, should provide adequate uplift, and certainly should not have a tight band under the bust. The Decreed pre-natal brassière, with adjustable cross-strap support, is stocked by the Treasure Cot shop at Daniel Neal's. After your baby is born, you can if you wish buy a special nursing brassière with front fastening, but in many cases the brassière that you wore beforehand will be perfectly suitable for the nursing period if you slip pads of folded gauze into the cups, to absorb any leakage of surplus milk.

Whether or not you need a maternity belt will depend very much on the strength of your abdominal muscles. If you have not been accustomed to wearing any but the narrowest belt, and this is your first baby, you may well find that you need no special abdominal support. You can deal with the problem of keeping up your stockings by wearing a hose-supporter such as Sleek-line. You may, however, find that you become rather tired in the later months of pregnancy and would welcome some support. Many of the well-known firms which specialise in foundation garments produce maternity belts, usually made with adjustable side lacings ; for those who need a light-weight belt there is one made in Aertex fabric.

It is not essential to have special lingerie for maternity wear, if you have loosely fitting garments. But you can if you wish either buy or make a wrap-round slip, and panties with adjustable side fastenings. If you plan to have new nightdresses they should be cut loose and full, and should be made in a style suitable to wear

during the nursing period ; they can fasten on the
shoulders or be made with a yoke, with a deep neck
opening. If you are going to have your baby in a
hospital where patients are expected to bring their own
nightdresses, avoid over-frilly styles which will quickly
lose their freshness, and filmy materials.

The last three months

This is the time when the change in your figure will
necessitate special styles of clothes. The danger here is
to get into one garment and stay in it, or to feel that
you are condemned to a maternity " uniform." Yet at
the cost of a little ingenuity, and by paying attention to
variety in your accessories and to pretty touches, you
can always look fresh and attractive.

Dress : The most adaptable wear of all is a two-piece
outfit. You will probably need two skirts, one for day-
time wear and another one for evenings. If you have
them made with a window front, they retain their even
hem-line and look attractively slim. Ready-made skirts
are available with adjustable slide fasteners, which equally
make for a slim fitting. Working on this basis, you can
achieve as much variety as you like with tunics and
smocks, adding different touches of detail. For day-time
wear, for instance, you might choose a swing-back jacket
to match your skirt, made in a button-through style,
with either a large or a small collar, or if you prefer it,
with a stand-up coolie collar ; or you may decide on
a contrast by having a jacket made of check material to
wear with your plain skirt.

Tunics are most useful. They can be flared or made with inverted pleats springing from a round or straight yoke. Give them important pockets, wear a gay bow at the neck or have them open-necked, with a tucked-in scarf. Make use of detachable collars and cuffs, which look crisp and fresh. There are endless possibilities if you own a sleeveless tunic with scooped-out neck-line : for day-time, a blouse or sweater looks well underneath it, or it can be worn with a pretty necklace for evening occasions. The problem of more formal evening dress can be solved by a tunic of brocade or other rich material, worn with a full-length window-front skirt.

Modern smocks, worn just long enough to cover the window front of the skirt, can look very attractive, and allow plenty of scope for variety in fabric and design. They might, for instance, be designed with short, set-in sleeves, or be made in magyar style, with a wide neck-line and no front opening,

If for some occasions you feel happier in a one-piece garment, there are attractive rayon or woollen dresses available, with adjustable waist-lines. A dress-length house-coat, worn unbelted, is comfortable to wear round the house. This style could be carried out in a rich velvet or corduroy for winter ; for summer a pretty cotton would look fresh and cool.

Most good dress shops stock a supply of maternity wear, but if you cannot manage to get to your local town, remember the shops which specialise in maternity wear by post, such as the Treasure Cot shop at Daniel Neal's, 3–7 Portman Square, W.1 (and branches) ; Du

Barry, 68 Duke Street, W.1 ; Restcots, 16-17 Orchard
Street, W.1 ; Maternally Yours, Ltd., 65 Weymouth
Street, W.1. For a list of retailers stocking Maxlim
models, write to Maxwell, Cooper & Co. Ltd., 5 Poland
Street. W.1.

If you decide to make your own outfits (which is the
least expensive course), there are many attractive styles
in dresses, two-piece sets, etc., produced by the paper
pattern manufacturers.

Outdoor wear : Modern styles in coats are very kind
to the expectant mother. A loose-fitting coat, light or
heavy weight according to the season, is all that is
needed, with perhaps an extra short jacket for spring
and autumn.

Shoes : High heels can be a source of real discomfort
and even of danger to you. While you are carrying a
baby, your weight distribution is altered, and in order
to maintain your equilibrium, you will automatically
lean slightly backwards, thus putting an additional strain
on the muscles of your back, abdomen and thighs. High
heels accentuate this tendency, and often account for the
muscular cramps and headache experienced by some
expectant mothers during the later weeks. They can
even cause you to lose your balance and risk a fall.

From among the fashionable styles, you can choose
various types of flat-heeled shoes, which are ideal at this
time. If you are accustomed to shoes with a heel and
feel more comfortable in them, you can choose a medium
heel, of about $1\frac{1}{2}$ inches. There may be a slight tendency
for the feet to swell in the evenings, especially in the

later months, and it is always best then to change into very comfortable shoes.

Preserving your looks

Nature will more than preserve your looks during the nine months of waiting. Your figure will grow heavier, of course, but in compensation your face will have a radiance it has never had before. The skin may be clear, the eyes sparkling and the hair shining and colourful. This is not magic, but the inevitable result of the careful diet, exercise in the fresh air, regular rest and generally healthy life which you will be following for your own and baby's sake.

There are, however, some ways in which you can help your looks. Your skin and hair, for instance, may become rather drier than usual. This is quite normal during pregnancy, but you can help by giving a little extra lubrication. Cut out skin tonics and astringents if you normally use them. Always wash with warm water, not hot or cold, and use a good brand of soap. A soothing protective cream used as a powder foundation by day, and a lubricating skin food used as often as necessary at bedtime, will help to keep your complexion supple and glowing. Do not expose your skin to unkind weather without protection, and, above all, make sure it is very thoroughly cleansed at least twice a day.

Sometimes patches of brown discoloration appear on the face during pregnancy. Unfortunately there is nothing which can be done about this except to disguise them as far as possible with special make-up. They usually disappear after the baby is born.

The development of " stretch lines " on the abdomen and thighs can be discouraged by massaging the skin with warm olive oil two or three times a week, from the third month of pregnancy : this increases the elasticity of the skin.

Your hair will benefit from the use of a tonic, preferably one of a slightly oily type ; and occasionally, the night before a shampoo, you might massage in a generous amount of warmed olive oil.

If your hair is permanently waved, book a " perm " some time in the sixth month ; and at the same time have your hair cut as short as possible. In this way it will be easy to manage when you are in bed. For then, far from feeling too ill to care, you will feel refreshed and triumphant and wanting to look your best. Many women make an appointment for a trim, shampoo and set ten days or a week before baby is due, so that their hair looks neat and attractive when the time comes to receive visitors and congratulations.

Pay very special attention to your posture during the waiting months. An easy, upright carriage will not only give your appearance the dignity it should have at this time : it will actually help you through the physical changes your body experiences. The ante-natal exercises outlined on pages 26–28 will do much to help keep your posture good : and you can do even more by consciously correcting any tendency to " slump " at odd moments during the day. Even during the last months of your pregnancy it should be a matter of pride, as well as of good health sense, to hold yourself and your baby as well as you can.

Everything you can do to keep yourself pretty and well-groomed will pay good dividends in the extra feeling of self-confidence you will gain. Carefully tended hands and finger-nails, a pretty, neat hair style, immaculate lingerie touches—these details can make all the difference between an attractive expectant mother and that rather sad sight, a woman who has " let herself go."

The days spent in bed after your baby's arrival give you a unique opportunity to pander to your looks. Pack a few toilet essentials in a box to keep by your bedside : besides your comb and hair-brush, pins and curlers, include some pretty ribbons for your hair, your manicure things and some lavender water or eau de Cologne in liquid or solid form. A bottle of deodorant (or better still, a jar of deodorant cream) and a sprinkler tin of talcum will add the finishing touches to your daintiness and so to your peace of mind.

Planning and Furnishing
a Nursery

In most modern homes, one room must serve as the baby's day and night nursery, and later on it will become his playroom. It is important, however, that wherever possible, he should have this room of his own from his earliest days. If the only room available for a nursery is so placed that you are afraid you may not hear if the baby cries at night, you can usually install a " baby alarm," so that you can hear him from a distance.

The ideal aspect for a nursery is a south-easterly one : the room then gets the benefit of the morning sun and is cool in the afternoon. It is wise to guard the window ; one of the most attractive window-guards is made of strong flat steel decorated with scroll-work ; this can be easily screwed into the window-frame.

Heating

A baby sleeps most healthily in a pleasantly cool room ; a temperature of about 55° F. would be suitable for the night, while during the day a temperature of 60–65° F. is desirable. Background heating can be safely provided by a wall convector or an oil-filled sealed electric radiator. When the baby is being bathed or dressed this will need to be " topped up " with a radiant heater ; a wall-hanging reflector type, giving immediate heat where it is most needed, is a good choice. When electric fitments are used, it is always best to have them out of reach, and to use shuttered plugs for the nursery (see page 197). If the room is fitted with a gas or solid-fuel fire, this must be completely guarded.

Floor covering

The floor of a nursery should be easy to keep clean, and should provide a warm surface. Plastic flooring in sheet or tile form is excellent, and linoleum with an under-felt is a good alternative. Don't polish the floor—a slippery surface can easily cause accidents. Gay, washable rugs give a note of colour, and floor cushions covered in bright terry towelling are attractive and practical.

The walls

The treatment of the nursery walls is worth careful thought. Emulsion paint or hard gloss paint, though more expensive than distemper, is much to be preferred. Small fingers so very quickly mark distemper, and a certain amount of scribbling on the walls is almost inevitable, so the best way to avoid spoiled surfaces is to make them easily washable. You might arrange to have a plywood dado about three feet above the skirting along one wall ; it can be made with blackboard panels, covered with specially prepared black paper, and the rest of the dado can be used as a picture gallery for postcards and cut-outs.

As a rule, the nursery is a fairly small room, and you can best create a feeling of space by employing plain, light colours on the walls. For a sunny room, dove-grey or pale green are good colours. A room with less light would look better painted in pale pink or clear shades of pale yellow, but strong, sharp colouring creates the wrong effect. The ceiling can be painted to tone with the walls.

As an alternative to paint, wall-paper can look most attractive and is very serviceable. One good idea is to emphasise the wall on which interest is mainly focused, perhaps by using wall-paper with a simple all-over motif, and to cover the other walls with plain textured paper.

A frequent mistake is to over-elaborate the decoration of the nursery. Some wall-paper designs are too " busy," paint can be too white and glossy, and there are often too many fussy stencilled designs, perhaps showing grotesque figures. The result is restless and over-stimulating, or even frightening to a small child. A nursery is essentially a place for sleep and play ; its atmosphere should be peaceful, but gay and cosy—above all it should be a place where the child, as he develops, can use his own imagination.

Bright touches of colour can be introduced into the curtains. Nursery curtains should be easily washable ; unless they are made of a substantial fabric, it is best to line them, so that the room can be darkened.

Pictures : Hang the pictures low enough on the walls for a toddler to be able to enjoy them. There is a good selection available of prints of pictures by children's artists; an effective alternative is to mount gaily coloured posters on board, changing them from time to time. Bold, clear design should be your aim in choosing pictures for the nursery.

Furniture

In planning the nursery, you should look ahead to the days when it will be used as a playroom as well as a bedroom. At first, all you will need, besides the cot and a nursing chair, will be either a tall-boy or a chest-of-drawers for storing clothes. Later on, a wardrobe with hanging and shelf space can be added if there is no built-in cupboard. An adaptable chair-cum-table will be most useful in the toddler days. Nursery furniture can either be painted to a specific colour scheme, or natural waxed wood can be used to good effect.

As the child's personal possessions increase and his interests widen, he will need low shelves and cupboards for his books, toys and hobbies.

Sharing a room

If it is decided that the baby shall share the mother's room during his early months, the arrangement of the room is even more important. In this case, the cot should be put near the window, just out of the main draught, but not with the mother's bed placed between the cot and the ventilation from the window. A screen should be placed round the head of the cot, and the light should be shaded.

Baby's Layette and Nursery Equipment

Naturally you will be anxious for your baby to have everything he needs, and for his clothes and other equipment to look attractive as well as being practical. You may easily become confused by a great variety of advice : ideas on baby's needs have changed since your mother's day, and your own friends all have their particular preferences, which are not always suitable for your circumstances.

The layette

You can of course buy all baby's layette ready-made from a baby specialist shop or from the baby linen department of a big store. Many young mothers, however, delight in making most of the baby's clothes, and this is not only an economy, but it enables you to choose the styles you like best. Much will depend on how much time you have available and on whether you like knitting or sewing. Don't be discouraged if you are not very expert ; baby clothes are simple to make, and this is a good time to begin.

The main principle to remember in planning the layette is that the heat-regulating mechanism of a tiny baby's body is not yet completely functioning, so that his clothes must keep him warm ; moreover, the climate of this country is temperate and changeable. At the same time, all that baby wears should be light and porous. His clothes should never be tight, and they must be large enough to allow for some growth, but you do not want to swamp him in garments which are so large and shapeless that they are worn out before he has " grown into " them. Above all, remember that baby's skin is extremely delicate, and everything which touches it must be very soft. A good baby wool can be used with confidence for his vests ; wool "breathes" in a way which a synthetic fibre does not.

The basic layette for a summer or a winter baby is very similar ; fine woolly vests and gowns made of a wool and cotton mixture fabric are suitable for both. The summer baby will not need petticoats, bonnets, mitts or small head shawls (unless he is premature). We list here the articles necessary from birth to four months.

Layette for a summer baby

4–5 gowns	4–5 pairs bootees
4 vests	24 terry towelling
3 matinee coats	napkins
1 shawl or pram rug	24 gauze napkins

Layette for a winter baby

4–5 gowns	4–5 pairs bootees
4 vests	2 bonnets
2 petticoats	3 pairs mitts
3–4 matinee coats	24 terry towelling
1 shawl or pram rug	napkins
2 small head shawls	24 gauze napkins

You will also need well-cut waterproof baby pants in a small size.

Gowns : The plan which is most usually adopted is to dress the baby in the same type of gown all round the clock for the first three or four months, until he grows more active and needs short clothes in the day-time. He will be lying down and asleep most of the time during the day in these months, so that there is no point in elaborating his clothes, though you may like to smarten the gowns he wears in the day-time with a little embroidery. Even for a summer baby, gowns of wool and cotton mixture are the wisest choice—Clydella or Osmalane fabric in cream or pastel colours are hygienic and pretty, besides wearing well. For very special occasions, you might have one gown of lawn or nylon.

There are several good styles to choose from for the gowns. You can make these very simply in magyar or raglan style, or, if you prefer it, have set-in sleeves and a yoke on to which a plain skirt is gathered. If they are made with plenty of room for growth, they can be used as nightgowns for as long as eighteen months. It is a sensible idea to make the gowns open all the way down the back, fastening them only with three buttons at the top, so that they can be turned aside to avoid dampness. A ribbon fastening sewn on at the neck-edge is to be preferred to a draw-string, which might possibly be pulled tight and hurt the baby. Patterns for a raglan and a magyar-type gown are given at the end of the book.

Vests : Soft woollen vests are the best choice for the new baby. Good ready-made vests are obtainable in

THE NURSERY AND EQUIPMENT

On these four pages is shown some of the varied equipment now obtainable. The wicker nursing chair (which matches the cot shown overleaf) has a useful drawer. The pulp bath has its own stand, with soap-dish, towel-rail and a tray below. An alternative bath is a plastic folding type, to fit over any standard-size bath; it is easily filled and emptied. Yet another folding bath, with its own stand, is seen in the nursery pictured overleaf; this model has an emptying device.

Plate

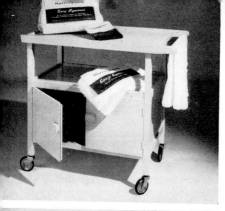

Plate II

The nursery trolley (*top*) is invaluable for holding all the baby's toilet accessories, napkins, etc. A screen is a useful addition in any nursery. The strong, light-weight wicker cot has a stand of its own.

Plate III

In the nursery above a carry-cot on a stand is protected from draughts by the screen. The bath, trolley, nursing chair, etc., are conveniently grouped for bath-time; a radiant heater on the wall gives warmth where it is most needed. Other points to notice are the capacious clothes airer, the attractive cupboard fitment, and the practical lino tiles. (See overleaf for alternative version.)

A weatherproof travelling cot can also serve as crib for the first few months. When choosing a pram, look for good springs and brake; for sunny days a lined canopy is needed. The picture below shows the nursery on the previous page adapted for an older baby, with a cot replacing the crib. As the baby can now go in the ordinary big bath, a special small bath is no longer necessary.

Plate IV

either a cross-over or an envelope-neck style. The vests can also be hand-knitted, either in a cross-over style or with a neck opening : if the former style is chosen, the cross-over should be ample and the vest made with a fairly high neck, to give enough protection to the baby's chest. Vests should be long enough to cover the baby's tummy, but not so long that they become damp : ten inches is an average length.

Petticoats : These are not a " must " in the layette, but they are a useful addition. They can be made in loosely woven flannel (about sixteen inches or so in length), and are used when an extra layer is needed in cold weather. They come in useful, too, for a girl baby of four months onwards on cool days when she is dressed in a light-weight frock for special occasions.

Matinee coats : Modern mothers demand that the baby's little jackets shall be practical as well as pretty, giving protection where it is needed over the chest, and they should be neither tight nor shapeless. When the baby is out in his pram (or for that matter when it is cool indoors) he should wear as his top layer of clothing either a snug woollen jacket or one made from the same material as the gowns. The sleeves should be wide enough to go over the gowns comfortably. Since ribbons are only chewed or dribbled on, three neat buttons make a much more effective fastening. If you prefer it, you can make first-size cardigans in either button-through or hug-me-tight style. Continental babies wear little jackets buttoned down the back, and this idea may appeal to mothers here. Our design (see plate XIII) may be worn either way, as preferred.

Shawls : There is no hard-and-fast rule about the kind of shawl which a small baby needs, and indeed it is possible to dispense with them altogether. Much will depend on your own circumstances. A large shawl is useful when the baby is being carried in the house, particularly if it is draughty, or when, for instance, he has to be undressed at the Clinic ; it will also do service as an extra cot covering, though it could be replaced by a soft pram rug. A knitted shawl should be chosen in a close pattern, without holes in which the baby can entangle his fingers. For a winter baby or a premature baby, you will find a couple of small head shawls very useful in the first month or two for wrapping closely round the baby when he is in his cot or pram and during feeds ; they should be about twenty-two inches square, either made of soft flannel or knitted in a simple pattern.

Bootees : A tiny baby's feet easily get cold except in hot weather, and he needs to wear woollen bootees which fit snugly round the ankles, with a crocheted draw-string round them. Long bootees are a good idea when baby begins to kick actively and the weather is cool.

Mitts are essential in cold weather ; make them without thumbs for the young baby, and draw them up securely at the wrists, also with a crocheted draw-string. Chilprufe make mitts for indoor wear, to prevent the baby from scratching his face, as he so easily tends to do.

A Bonnet is only needed out of doors when there is a keen wind blowing. A cap with ear-flaps, fastening under the chin, is a good type to use for the baby boy.

Napkins : Terry towelling napkins worn over gauze napkins are the most usual choice. The baby's skin is very delicate and needs the softness of the gauze napkins, while the terry towelling is necessary to absorb the moisture. It is a labour-saving idea to buy rolls of cellulose wadding from the chemist, and to slip a small piece inside each clean napkin, disposing of it after use. As the gauze napkins are more quickly washed and dried than the thicker terry towelling, you may feel that you can manage with fewer of these, but you will find the extra ones are invaluable as an undersheet for the baby in cot or pram, or they can be used as bibs or face towels.

There are bound to be times when it is not possible or convenient to do baby's daily washing, and for these times, or for occasions when you are visiting with baby, you may like to keep a small stock of disposable napkins, consisting of a cellulose pad and plastic pants.

Protective waterproof baby pants : In recent years these have greatly improved and fulfil a very useful function. A conscientious mother will in any case change and cleanse her baby at frequent intervals, and with these precautions there is no reason why she should not make discriminating use of protective garments for the baby. The pants should be cut to ensure the maximum possible ventilation consistent with adequate protection, and there should be no pressure which is likely to chafe the baby's legs. Fine quality plastic and even nylon-covered plastic are effectively used in various makes now on the market, and there are pretty frilly ones for little girls.

The second stage

From four months the baby will become much more vigorous, so he will need more freedom for his limbs and at the same time more protection if the weather is cold. Here is a list of essentials :

4 second-size vests

3 16-inch frocks ⎫
2 petticoats ⎭ For a girl

3 one- or two-piece rompers, ⎫
    smocked tunics or jerseys ⎭ For a boy

4 pairs baby pants

2 outdoor pram sets (cool weather)

Bonnet, mitts, bootees, as before

Sleeping-bag (cool weather)

Napkins (as before)

6 bibs

3 pairs dungarees (from about nine months)

This is the time to change from gowns to short clothes for day-time wear. Baby girls will wear sixteen-inch first-size frocks in cotton, silk or one of the synthetic fibre materials, made perhaps with a smocked or embroidered yoke. Little boys can be suitably dressed in one- or two-piece rompers, a smocked tunic, or a neat jersey, and pilch-type knickers to keep nappies in place.

From the time the baby begins to crawl, he will need washable dungarees, made of cotton in a practical colour for the summer months, or of warmer cloth for winter.

For outdoor wear in cold weather, a child of this age needs outdoor pram sets, consisting of a warm knitted jacket with a collar, and leggings with feet for wearing in the pram. As knitted coats do not give full protection against the wind, the baby should wear a fabric dress or romper under his coat. From about nine to twelve months, a simple fabric coat can replace the knitted one, though it is better to keep to knitted leggings as long as they need frequent washing. As with the younger baby, a bonnet or helmet and mitts are also needed.

It can be quite difficult to keep an active older baby—from about nine months—covered in bed. A good idea is to buy or make nightgowns which are buttoned along the bottom hem, as this keeps baby's feet warm.

Baby-bags : A baby-bag is most useful in the cold weather, for the child from about four months. It can either be bought or made at home from soft woollen fabric, and can fasten over the shoulders with buttons or down the front with a zip fastening. It is advisable to attach a piece of easily changeable waterproof material inside the back of the bag, as a protection. Kamella make one with a collar and a detachable flap at the base, so that it can be adapted for use as a dressing-gown later on. Baby-bags should ideally be kept just for day-time use in the pram, and not be used at night in the cot, as the baby tends to become over-heated, and also everything which he wears at night must be readily washable.

Clothes for babies in hot climates

Babies brought up in tropical or sub-tropical conditions need only very light clothing. It is impossible to be quite specific, as conditions vary widely ; even in equatorial regions the climate may be quite cool in the hills, and the degree of humidity of the atmosphere has also to be taken into account. If you are going out to a tropical country, therefore, inform yourself beforehand on local conditions. The Royal Commonwealth Society, 18 Northumberland Avenue, W.C.2, will provide useful information on Commonwealth countries.

In hot weather a baby will only need to wear a napkin and perhaps a cellular cotton vest. A small boy can be dressed in a cotton sun-suit, and a girl in a cotton frock and knickers. Children should usually wear a shady cotton hat out of doors. In cooler weather, clothes similar to those worn in England may be needed.

In countries where infection by hookworm or bilharzia is common, children should never be allowed to discard shoes or socks when they are walking.

Only a very light-weight sheet or even no bedding at all is needed in hot weather. For the cooler season, Clydella cot sheets and one cot-size cellular wool blanket would be adequate.

Nursery equipment

There is a wide choice of attractive equipment available, and you need to make quite certain that you choose only items from which you will get full use and value. You will be guided in your choice by the circumstances of your own life ; if you have limited storage space, for instance, you will want a small, compact pram, and if you want the baby to travel with you by car, a portable cot will be your choice. In all you buy avoid fussy details, and aim at easily cleaned equipment.

The choice of a cot

A baby really needs a small cot for the first few months, to give him the comfort and sense of security of a nest. Many mothers like to have this cot light in weight so that they can easily move it from place to place. A good choice is a wicker cradle on a stand ; it is stable, and yet allows the free circulation of air. An Italian cradle of plaited straw is a suitable alternative.

A popular type of first crib is a carry-cot of fabric or plastic duck (supplied either with or without a hood and storm-apron). It is easily carried from nursery to living-room, it can be placed on the back seat of a car, and is recommended for babies travelling by air. Some carry-cots have their own stands, and standard-sized carry-cots will fit on to the stand of a polythene bath now available.

The first cot will normally last the baby until he is about five months, when he changes to a drop-side cot.

How to make up the cot : Essential bedding consists of :

    A hair, rubberised hair or latex foam mattress

    A waterproof sheet (about 18 by 27 inches)

    3 under-sheets (napkins can be used)

    2 flannelette blankets (about 40 by 60 inches)

    3 light-weight or cellular wool cot blankets (white or pastel-coloured)

    1 washable cot cover.

The mattress for a baby's cot needs to be firm, in order to give good support to his back, and it should be well ventilated. The choice lies between a mattress filled with hair or rubberised hair, or one made from latex foam, all of which fill these requirements. The

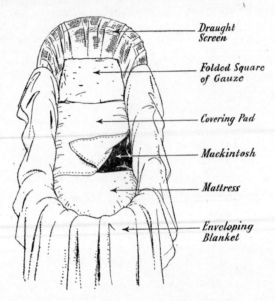

Draught Screen

Folded Square of Gauze

Covering Pad

Mackintosh

Mattress

Enveloping Blanket

MAKING BABY'S BED. The big enveloping blanket goes in first, then the mattress, waterproof sheet and under-sheet (a napkin may be used for this). When baby lies in the cradle, wrapped in shawl or soft blanket, the two sides of the enveloping blanket are folded over him, and the foot is tucked in like an envelope. A soft, light-weight cellular blanket and a pretty, washable cover are then placed on top.

standard measurements for a first-size cot are 33 inches by 15 inches.

It is best for a baby up to a year old to have no pillow, as there is a danger of his suffocating if he should bury his face in a soft one. If you like, you can put a folded square of gauze under his head. For the method of making the bed, see sketch opposite.

The drop-side cot :   At about five nonths baby will need to sleep in a drop-side cot. The usual size is 4 feet by 2 feet. The wood can either be finished in natural wax, or it can be enamelled in shades to tone with the nursery furnishing scheme. (Incidentally, if baby cuts his teeth on the bars of the cot, and it becomes necessary to re-paint it at home, you should make certain that you use a lacquer with a safe leadless base.) A point of safety to consider is the width between the bars, as there is a possibility that an active child may get his limbs stuck between them if they are too widely spaced ; about 3–3¾ inches is the usual spacing, and the gaps certainly should not exceed this. The side which drops should be fitted with a secure catch.

It is important to provide a firm hair or latex foam cot mattress. The necessary bed-clothes for the cot consist of two pairs of sheets, usually of flannelette, a water-proof sheet and under-sheets as long as they are needed, and light-weight blankets and cot cover. The drop-side cot should remain in use until the child is about three years of age, after which he can be promoted to a child's bed with safety sides, or to a 2 ft. 6 in. divan with a firm mattress.

B.B.—5

Bath-time equipment

In a warm and convenient corner, you can assemble all the equipment you need for bathing and feeding baby.

If the bathroom is adequately warmed, you may like to have your centre of operations here. A folding plastic bath fitted over the ordinary bath meets the situation admirably. Alternatively, you may prefer to bath the baby in a corner of the nursery, protected by a screen. You may choose a plastic or rubber bath, which is soft and can be folded away when not in use, or you may like to have a light-weight sprayed metal bath or a papier mâché one. In all cases, it is most useful to have a stand for the bath.

A low, comfortable nursery chair is a boon at bath and feeding times. It should give good support for your back and freedom for your arms.

An important point to consider is where you will keep all the numerous accessories which baby needs when he is being bathed, dressed and fed. If you and baby are both going to enjoy bath-time in peace, you will want to have everything immediately at hand for your use, and if your nursery is to be kept neat and hygienic, it is just as important that you have somewhere to put soiled articles immediately.

You can deal with this question in a variety of ways, some very simple, others more elaborate. A nursery trolley with shelf and cupboard space is the most complete answer. The top shelf, spread with a napkin, can be used while you are drying or dressing the baby. On the lower shelf you have his cream, powder, lotion, cotton-wool, safety-pins, his nail scissors and brush and comb. His clean clothes and napkins can be stored in the cupboard. A two-tier trolley serves the purpose quite adequately, with a small clothes airer for clothes. Simplest of all would be a glass shelf in the bathroom, or an enamel tray in the nursery. A covered pail takes soiled napkins.

A nursery screen is useful at bathing-time, as well as for protecting the cot. You can easily make one at home by using a good-sized three-fold clothes airer, and covering it with washable cotton material doubled over the top of the screen and sewn down the sides. The cover can be quickly removed for washing.

A terry towelling apron with detachable plastic back is an excellent idea for use while bathing the baby, as the terry towelling can, if necessary, be boiled.

The baby will need his own bath and face towels ; the softest type is made of two- or three-fold gauze.

These, then, are the items which you will need :

Nursing-chair

Three-fold screen

Towel rail or clothes airer

Nursing apron

Pail with lid

Chamber-pot

Bath thermometer (optional)

Receptacle for accessories, e.g. two-tier trolley

Jar with lid for cotton-wool swabs

Baby lotion, cream and powder

Curved nursery safety-pins

Baby soap

Soft hair-brush

Comb

Nail scissors

Baby scales (optional— may be hired if necessary).

Choosing your pram

It will be a matter of pride to take your baby out in a good-looking pram, but there are other considerations as well—comfort, smooth running, safety and durability, as well as expense and storage space. It is always advisable to order your pram in good time if you want a particular style and colour ; most shops will give you a guarantee that it can be returned in case it is not needed.

The first important decision is between a high pram and a low drop-end one. If you can spare the storage space and the extra money which a high pram costs, it does provide additional warmth and comfort for the baby, and is probably more convenient to push if you are fairly tall. Some high prams are fitted with extensions, which are useful as the baby grows, especially if you want him to sleep outside in his pram. Most low prams have a drop-end which may be adapted in two positions when the child sits up.

Having decided on the type of pram you want, you can make your choice between a coach-built or a metal-bodied pram, or (so far as some low prams are concerned), between a fabric, a plastic duck or a P.V.C. body. If you choose a reliable make—and this is important on every score—any of these materials should give good wear.

There are a number of special points to consider about the pram. The bed-length should not be less than 32 inches ; some are 34 or 36 inches. The average width is about 15 inches. Most high prams have C-springs and strap suspension, which makes for smooth, easy running ; a few low prams are sprung on the same principle, while others have coil springs.

When you are buying a pram, make quite sure that it is well balanced and has very effective brakes—this is more important than the amount of chrome on the pram fittings ! An active baby and the toddler brother are sure to try their hardest on some occasion to overturn the pram. The brakes usually act on two wheels, and their action should be tested. Some prams have an anti-tip device, others can have one fitted, while some rely on good balance to counteract tipping. A well-balanced pram has resilience, and is neither heavy nor rigid.

A useful idea included in some low prams is to have a detachable body, which can be used as a carry-cot when the baby is small. This is a great convenience for car or air-travel (especially as the carry-cot is not considered as extra luggage), or if the pram must be carried upstairs.

In sunny weather the pram will need to be fitted with a lined pram canopy to protect the baby from glare. A matching pram apron is smart and cool. The pram hood should only be raised when it is raining or if a very cold wind is blowing, and the waterproof apron is only used as a protection against wet weather. Where there is a danger of cats jumping on to the pram while the baby is outside, a net should be fitted over it. A pram bag, fastened on to the end of the pram, is a convenience.

Pram bedding : The pram, like the cot, will need a firm mattress, waterproof sheet and under-sheet, and will also need a pram rug. During the first year the baby should have no pillow in his pram (although it is a good plan to put his head on a firm pillow immediately after a feed, then the pillow can be placed at the end of the pram while he is sleeping). From about four months old the baby can be kept comfortably warm during cold weather in a baby-bag.

Care of the pram : Like all good equipment, a pram needs to be carefully maintained. If the coach-work is dirty after rain, it should be washed over with a sponge and cold water, and dried with a wash leather. Marimo cloth hoods should be brushed with an average clothes brush. When necessary, they can be lightly scrubbed (in one direction) at frequent intervals with plenty of cold or lukewarm water and a medium nail-brush, then left stretched to dry. Plastic duck or P.V.C. linings can be treated by light brushing with a used nail-brush and mild household soap and dried with a clean cloth. Do not use any detergents, furniture cream or oily polishes. Don't forget to dry chrome parts thoroughly if they are damp ; they can be rubbed up about once a month with a proprietary chrome cleaner. It is best to ask your retailer for advice on the care of your pram.

Push-chairs : From the time the baby can walk, he will need a light push-chair, for short journeys. There is a wide selection available, some with full weather protection, others with quick-folding action, which makes them suitable for taking on public vehicles, some made of canvas and light-weight metal which are light and easy to manage.

Where there are both a toddler and a baby, you may find the best solution is a toddler's seat on baby's pram.

The Birth of the Baby

As the last month begins, you will be glad to feel that
the end of your waiting-time is approaching. Most of
your preparations will naturally be completed by now,
but this is the time to check them and make any necessary
final arrangements. As you cannot be certain of the
exact date of baby's birth, you should be as ready as
possible about a fortnight before the expected date.

You will want to confirm the domestic arrangements
you have made to cover the lying-in period. If you
have a toddler in the home, he should now be gently
prepared for this time and should be given a chance to
get to know whoever will be looking after him.
Wherever possible, let your deputy spend a day in the
home with you, so that she will know your routine.

If you are going into hospital or a nursing home, your
suitcase should be ready packed at this time. If you
are having the baby at home, check over the items in
your accouchement set and make sure that the bedroom
can be prepared at short notice. It is best to strip the
room of all ornaments and oddments from shelves and
tables, and to clear the floor as much as possible. If you
have linoleum or plastic flooring on the floor, that is
ideal ; a carpet usually needs to be covered with an old
sheet or a layer of brown paper.

A single bed is best of all for a confinement, and if
possible it should not be too low.

If a drawer in your dressing-table or wardrobe can be

cleared to take a supply of clean linen and towels, your midwife will bless you for the thought. A table must be arranged conveniently near to the bed for the washing arrangements, and should be covered with a clean cloth.

Requirements for the confinement

In a hospital : In a hospital you do not need any clothing for yourself, or for baby, during the two weeks you are there, though you will naturally have to provide a complete set of clothes for baby to go home in. It is permissible to have one or two pretty bed-jackets of your own to wear over hospital nightdresses, and in some hospitals you may wear your own nighties, but as frequent changes are necessary, you have to make your own arrangements for laundering. You may be asked to take in with you two or three packets of sanitary towels, and it is advisable to provide yourself with a card of large safety-pins. Many hospitals give the expectant mother a short list of the necessities which she must bring with her.

You will, of course, take your own toilet accessories, the " beauty box " mentioned on page 49, some knitting or sewing to do during convalescence and a book or two (though many hospitals have a library services).

In a nursing home or hospital private ward : The matron will provide you with a list of requirements, which will be somewhat as follows :—

For yourself :

4 nightdresses (1 old)	Dressing-gown and slippers
1 bedjacket	Sanitary towels

For baby :

4 vests	3–4 dozen napkins (some Turkish,
4 nightgowns	some gauze)

Sponge, soap, powder and cream

All the garments and napkins must be clearly marked with your surname. The nightdresses should be suitable for nursing purposes, opening down the front or tied on the shoulders with new ribbon straps. They should be of material that washes easily and well. One or two spare bed-jackets, while not essential, are advisable.

For a confinement at home : Here are general hints :

Complete sterilised sets (accouchement sets) containing the necessities for the actual confinement are supplied through the Welfare Centre, and are free for those having their confinement under the Health Service Act arrangements. Otherwise, sets costing up to about £5 may be obtained from chemists or stores. An accouchement set should only be opened by the midwife.

An accouchement outfit as supplied by the Ministry of Health contains :

1 gamgee accouchement sheet

1 lb. cotton-wool

1 dozen large sanitary towels

2 dozen smaller sanitary towels

1 sheet of waterproofed brown paper

1 crepe bandage, 3-inch (for baby's binders)

Safety-pins

Cord powder and dressings

Linen thread for cord ligatures

Dettol is also supplied in some areas.

Requisites needed to supplement the accouchement outfit are :

    2 dozen large sanitary towels and belt
    1 accouchement sheet
    1 rubber hot-water bottle
    2 new nail-brushes
    Rubber sheeting ($1\frac{1}{2}$ yards)
    Bed pan (may be hired from chemist)
    Dettol
    Medicine glass
    Bedroom jug and basin (if available)
    2 or 3 enamel bowls (14 inches in diameter)
    2 enamel jugs, 2 pint (one only if bedroom jug available)
    1 covered slop-pail
    2 face-cloths and 1 larger cloth
    Toilet soap
    1 clean thin blanket for bed-bath
    2 binders for mother (optional)
    3 or 4 drawsheets (made from old sheets)
    A good supply of towels, sheets, pillow-cases and nightdresses
    Small bottle of olive oil
    Needle and white cotton for baby's binder
    Baby's toilet requisites, as detailed on page 67.

How will baby be born ?

When the longed-for time arrives at last, the powerful muscles of the uterus start to contract in order to push the baby downwards, while the cervix or neck of the womb dilates to allow him to pass down through the vagina. Later, the abdominal muscles are also brought into play.

The first signs of labour : It is often rather a worry to the expectant mother to know whether labour has really begun or not. And so it may help you if the signs are listed here :

(*a*) The regular occurrence of contractions in the lower abdomen which pass right round to the back. At first, these will occur spasmodically, but gradually they become more regular, so that if you keep an eye on the clock you can work out how often they come. When they are occurring every 5–10 minutes, you can be sure that you are in labour. There may be a slight discomfort, similar to that experienced during a period, but the anticipation and joy you feel quite discount it. If you place your hand on your tummy during a contraction, you will feel it harden.

(*b*) Very often the contractions are the first sign, then you notice a little blood and mucus coming from the front passage. This is commonly known as " a show," and really means that the canal in the cervix (or neck of the womb) is beginning to dilate or open.

(*c*) Sometimes the first sign is the sudden and uncontrollable loss of water from the front passage (or vagina), which means that the bag of water has burst, and that soon you may expect to commence having contractions. Often the membranes do not break until the first or second stage of labour is well advanced ; but if they break at the very beginning it is always wise to tell your doctor or midwife at once, and if they wish it, go to hospital or nursing home as you have arranged. Do not forget, if this is your second baby, that labour may not be so long as it was with your first, so call in the doctor or midwife in good time.

If the mother understands what is happening, she will be able to help enormously by co-operating with the natural processes. When the contractions occur she can feel glad that each one is bringing the baby one step nearer, and when the cervix is fully dilated, she can assist by pushing with her abdominal muscles. Between the contractions, which occur rhythmically, she can relax as she has learnt to do during her pregnancy (see page 28), knowing that this will in turn allow easy expansion of the tissues around the vagina through which the baby has to pass. Conversely, if she allows herself to be tense or frightened, these passages tighten up, and she is actually delaying the longed-for arrival of her baby, and incidentally greatly increasing the pain and discomfort. No one should minimise the effort which is demanded from a mother during her labour, but if she faces it with understanding, co-operation and courage, she can make the birth of her baby one of the most triumphant and satisfying experiences of her life.

The first stage of labour: You may be able to go about your work at first if labour begins during the day-time. At first the contractions are not always very strong, but they can often be helped by taking a dose of castor oil, and then after this has acted, by immersion in a hot bath and having an enema. All these things may be ordered by your nurse or doctor, and are always supervised by the nurse in charge, and they certainly do help matters when labour is rather slow in beginning. If you haven't had an enema before, you may find it slightly unpleasant, but it will not be painful. (Your nurse will also probably shave the pubic hairs, so that the area can be kept scrupulously clean.)

When the contractions begin to get really strong and regular, you will probably want to rest and relax, so if you feel like it do not hesitate to ask to go to bed. It is most important that you should not get over-tired during this stage, which normally lasts from 12 to 24 hours in the case of a first baby. Sometimes it is longer and sometimes much shorter, but the latter part of this stage, when the cervical canal is really getting fully dilated, is perhaps the most uncomfortable time of all. It is here that the woman who has practised relaxation during her pregnancy will benefit so much. She will tend to be calmer and more confident, and this stage will pass more quickly because there is little tension to hinder the birth processes.

If you need it, it is more than likely that the doctor or midwife will give you a sedative during the latter part of the first stage, and this will help you to rest well between the contractions and also to co-operate well during the contractions.

A change of posture will often help to make the contractions more bearable, and may also help to speed up the birth of the child. You may find that it helps if you lean on your hands, pressing them on a table or window-sill; or you may find that it is better to sit down and lean forward, resting the elbows on a table, or even to squat down on your haunches.

The second stage of labour : During this stage the bag of membranes and the baby's head are being pushed down into the vagina by the increasingly powerful contractions, and will gradually dilate the vaginal passage and so make their appearance.

The character of the contractions changes and you are conscious of a desire to help in expelling your child, and so quite naturally you begin to push down with each one.

During this stage the baby gradually dilates the outlet and is born. Usually the head comes first, to be followed by the shoulders and the rest of the body. The cord attaching it to the after-birth is then tied and severed by the midwife or doctor.

The third stage : After 10 or 15 minutes of comparative inertia following baby's birth, the uterus begins to contract again. The doctor or midwife then usually helps matters by pressing firmly on the mother's abdomen to aid the expulsion of after-birth and membranes. This constitutes the third stage; after this you will be washed and made comfortable, given a hot drink and then allowed to rest and admire your baby.

Stitching : If the area around the vaginal outlet has torn a little during the birth, it will probably be stitched up again quite soon after the expulsion of the after-birth, or even before. An anæsthetic may not be necessary, because the whole area is often numb for a time, but if necessary the doctor will use a local anæsthetic. Sometimes during the birth and under an anæsthetic the doctor makes a deliberate enlargement of the outlet, instead of letting it tear irregularly. This is called an *Episiotomy*, and this too needs stitching up afterwards in the same way, but it is often done so soon that you know nothing about it until you are told afterwards.

" *After-pains* " : During the first 24 hours following baby's birth the mother may experience quite severe pains which come at intervals, and are often accompanied by the passage of one or two clots of blood. This is what is meant by the term " after-pains," but many women have them only very slightly or not at all, and in any case they can be relieved fairly easily.

After baby is born

At first you may experience a little difficulty in passing water and your bowels may not act until two or three days have passed ; these two symptoms are quite usual.

You will notice about the second day that your breasts begin to feel heavier, and by the third day they will be really full. At first the process of breast-feeding may be rather painful if the breasts are too full. If this is the case you may be advised to cut down your intake of liquids. Hand expression is the best way to deal with any surplus, and your midwife will see to this.

Post-natal depression : Some mothers are dismayed to find themselves tearful and depressed for some days, or even weeks, after the confinement, just when they expected to feel on top of the world. These are usually the alert and conscientious type, who have been keyed up during the pregnancy and anxious to do the right thing during the confinement—more keyed up than they realised. This has caused nervous exhaustion, and they need far more rest than hospitals and nursing homes usually afford. If you feel like this, you should realise the reason for your feelings and allow yourself opportunity for rest and relaxation when you return home ; if you do not worry, you will soon recover your poise. It is a mistake for you to feel that you must do everything yourself for the baby—you should accept offers of help, especially from your husband, and make up lost sleep.

You and your husband : Do not neglect all your outside interests, and above all do not neglect your marriage, for that relationship still needs nurture and care. The baby is the joy and responsibility of both of you, and your husband must never be made to feel that your interest in · the baby is exclusive and monopolising. Most husbands in these days enjoy helping with the family, and wise wives will turn a blind eye to early mistakes and clumsiness. Babies are quite tough enough to stand a little masculine handling at times.

It is not wise to recommence intercourse for at least one month after the baby is born ; the interval will probably be longer if the wife has had stitches. Do not worry if you have no conscious desire for this particular relationship for a few months after the baby's birth. This is quite a common experience, probably due to the sexual satisfaction which motherhood has brought, and also partly due to tiredness. If you can realise that your husband will still want to express his love for you in that way, and if you can receive it passively for a time for his sake, you will find that you will eventually respond again as before. (For those who wish it, confidential advice on spacing the family or on promoting fertility may be obtained from the Family Planning Association, 64 Sloane Street, London, S.W.1.)

How to regain your figure

This is a burning question with every mother. Do not forget that for several months after baby's arrival your figure may continue to alter, because the lower ribs, which have been splayed out during the latter months of pregnancy, do not fall back into place suddenly. The exercises listed here may be done in bed once the first two days are over, if the doctor or midwife allows. Massage of the abdomen and legs is also very helpful.

Lying on your tummy for at least an hour a day helps to restore muscle tone, and also ensures that the womb returns to its normal position. At all other times while you are still in bed, unless actually sleeping, you should be sitting up.

Breathing : Precede all periods of exercise with deep breathing. Towards the end of pregnancy breathing is apt to be more shallow, and it is easy to continue the habit. When lying in bed during the first few days or standing astride when you get up, place your hands just above the hips over the lower ribs, breathe in slowly, trying to push against your hands with your ribs, and breathe out. Repeat six times. During the following

B.B.—6

exercises continue to breathe evenly and deeply. All periods of exercise should be followed by complete relaxation, as you learnt during the ante-natal period.

Toning-up exercises

(see Plate XII)

Do exercises 1–4 in bed, starting the third day after the baby's birth, or earlier if given permission ; Nos. 5 and 6 may be done after the fifth day or so and Nos. 7–10 may be added when you are up.

Exercise 1 : With legs together and the hands down at each side, lift the head from the bed till the chin touches the chest ; let it go back and repeat five times in all. (See Figure 1.)

Exercise 2 : Still lying on your back, raise the right leg to an angle of forty-five degrees with the bed, point the toe fully and rotate the ankle as far as possible in each direction, curling up the toes when the sole faces inwards. Lower leg slowly, and repeat with other leg and foot ; do five times with each leg. (Figure 2.)

Exercise 3 : Roll over and lie face downwards. With your thighs and chest still touching the bed, pull in the tummy muscles so that you can get your hands between the bed and yourself quite easily. Hold muscles in while you count four, and relax. Repeat six times.

Exercise 4 : After a short period of rest, and still in the same position, clasp the hands behind the back and raise the shoulders off the bed, with the head held back. Relax, and repeat five times.

Practise the above exercises three times a day.

The following may be done at the end of the first week:

Exercise 5 : Lying on your back and keeping the head and shoulders on the bed, bend the arms, digging the elbows in the bed, then bend the knees and draw up the feet as far as possible, raising the trunk off the bed. Swing gently from side to side, five times each side, breathing deeply and evenly all the time. (Figure 3.)

Exercise 6 : Lie on your back and pedal an imaginary bicycle with one leg, bringing the knee right up to the chest and then fully stretching the leg and pointing the toe. Repeat with the other leg. When you feel able, ride up an imaginary hill with both legs working, but stop as soon as you feel tired or breathless. (Figure 4.)

These may be added to the above when you are up:

Exercise 7 : Standing with your feet apart and hands on hips, move the trunk forward to the left and slightly backward to the right in one circular movement slowly and evenly. Repeat three times and then three times in the opposite direction. (Figure 5.)

Exercise 8 : Kneel on the floor with your hands linked loosely behind you. Still kneeling, sit back on your heels and curl up until the top of your head is tucked down level with your knees. Straighten up slowly, and repeat five times. (Figure 6.)

Exercise 9 : This exercise is designed to restore the tone of the pelvic muscles, and should be done almost every hour from the beginning, provided there is no soreness. Many of the minor disabilities which follow childbirth are due to the sagging of these muscles. Practise drawing up the floor of the pelvis as though you were tightening the exits of bowel and bladder, or trying to squeeze the buttocks together. Hold while you count four and relax. Repeat six times.

Exercise 10 : This last exercise helps to get rid of the "spare tyre" and increases the tone of the abdominal muscles. Like Exercise 9, it should be done almost hourly from the beginning. Having breathed out, draw the tummy muscles inwards and upwards, making as much of a hollow beneath the breast bone as you can. Hold this while you count four and relax. You will be able to hold this for longer periods when you have become more practised. This has a massaging effect on the colon beneath, especially when the stomach is empty.

Diet

Whether or not you are breast-feeding, you should have an adequate diet, which will restore any mineral, protein and vitamin deficiencies caused by the demands of the baby. This means plenty of proteins, meat (including liver), eggs, cheese, fish, fruit and vegetables, and your vitamin supplements. But if you tend to be over-weight, there is no harm in reducing the amount of starches and fats, even if you are breast-feeding. (See list on page 25.)

You should continue to take your vitamin A and D tablets, which are supplied free for thirty weeks after the birth of your baby ; they are obtained from the Welfare Foods Distribution Centre by means of special tokens included with the Child's Milk Token Book.

The post-natal examination

It is most important for you to have an examination about six weeks after baby's arrival, and this should be arranged with the Post-natal Clinic or with your own doctor. Many a case of severe backache after childbirth could be prevented by undertaking this routine examination, as sometimes the womb does not go back to the correct position and may cause trouble later.

If you are breast-feeding baby, the periods will not usually start for at least five or six months. Should they start earlier, this is no reason for weaning baby, as there is no lasting effect on the composition of the milk.

If you are not breast-feeding, the periods should re-commence earlier, probably within six or eight weeks of the confinement.

The new-born baby

Although apparently so helpless, a new-born baby has some strong reflexes and instincts, and most of his senses are already awake.

He can see lights, and sometimes follows them with his eyes, but he hates a bright light.

He can hear immediately at birth or during the first fortnight, and is startled by loud noises.

He can smell and taste, and will search for his food with his mouth.

He can grip very strongly if you put your finger in his hand.

He can cry, and at this stage this is the only way of

expressing his feelings of fright, hunger and annoyance. Loud and long can he cry if necessary !

He can yawn and sneeze, and even hiccup occasionally.

He can suck, and this provides him with solace as well as food, hence the frequency with which his fingers and thumb find their way into his mouth.

Umbilical cord : This is the vital link between the mother's placenta and the baby's navel, through which he is nourished before birth. After the birth the cord is tied and cut a few inches from the baby. It dries up and separates spontaneously after a few days. Until this happens and the navel is quite normal, it should be powdered and covered with a dressing. A crêpe bandage makes a convenient binder to keep a dressing in place, but can be left off when the dressing is discarded.

Stools : During the first few days these consist of a black and tarry substance called *meconium.* Then they begin to change colour, and finally become bright yellow. During the first few weeks the stools may be very frequent. (See page 133 for fuller details.)

Weight loss : For various reasons a baby tends to lose a few ounces during the first few days, but usually starts to gain from the fourth day or so. Some have regained their birth weight by the tenth day, others take longer.

Is he normal ? Mixed with the joy and wonder of the first few hours is the anxiety in the mother's mind as to whether he is quite normal. There are all sorts of minor conditions that may be present at birth or a little later, which need explanation to those who are unaccustomed to seeing new babies.

His colour at first may dismay you, because he is so red, but after a few days he will look more normal. The skin often peels, and some of the hair may fall, but this is quite in order. A little jaundice is common on the second or third day, and is of no significance. But if it is actually present at birth or quite soon after, it may indicate some destruction of the red blood cells by antibodies in the mother's blood : your doctor will give the appropriate treatment if it appears necessary.

Storkbites : This is the name sometimes given to little reddish marks which may be present on the upper eyelids, at the back of the head, and in a V-shape on the forehead. They fade gradually during the first twelve months, and nothing need be done about them.

Birthmarks are more deeply coloured and have more clearly defined edges than storkbites. They may be bright red, port-wine or brown in colour. There is no evidence to support any of the old wives' tales which attempt to explain their origin, in fact no one knows the real cause. The bright red variety which are raised from the surface of the skin are the most common, and have the name of " strawbery nævus." These nearly always disappear spontaneously during the first few years, even though they often increase in size to start with. Your doctor will probably advise you to defer treatment for a while for these particular birthmarks. There are cosmetics on the market which will effectively cover any that may show.

Swellings on the head : A soft swelling may be present on the part of the head which was born first. It subsides

in time, and needs no treatment. More rarely a harder
swelling is present, and this also needs no treatment.

Many babies' heads are not quite symmetrical, and
sometimes one half may look quite squashed. This
nearly always rights itself as the baby sits up more, and
any residual asymmetry is concealed later by the hair.

Feet and legs : The lower parts of the legs are normally
curved a little ; true bow legs do not appear until much
later. If the feet turn in or appear otherwise abnormal,
report the fact to your doctor, who will arrange the
appropriate treatment to put them right. It may take
the form of splinting or plaster or simple massage, but
good results are obtained if treatment is begun early.

The neck muscles sometimes have a hard lump in them,
due to bruising of the muscles during birth. Show this
to your doctor, but treatment is rarely necessary, because
it disappears spontaneously during the first year. It is
usually advised to lay the baby on the affected side.

Swelling of the breasts : This is common in both baby
girls and boys, and a thin watery " milk," similar to the
mother's colostrum, may be secreted. It is believed to
be due to hormones from the mother circulating in the
baby's blood before birth. No treatment whatever is
needed, and the condition subsides in due course. More
rarely there may be a little blood-stained discharge from
the vagina in girl babies, likewise due to the influence
of hormones. Again, nothing need be done about it.

Tongue-tie : This may appear to be present because
the membrane which attaches the tongue to the floor of
the mouth may extend to the tip. But only if this very

definitely interferes with sucking need anything be done, and the " snipping " is an easy matter for your doctor. In most cases the tongue lengthens beyond this attachment as the baby grows.

The eyes are very often bluish in colour to start with, but more pigment may be laid down later and make them darker. They do not focus properly for a month or two, and so squinting may be common. Only if it persists after three or four months need advice be sought.

Circumcision : The attitude of doctors to circumcision has changed during the past few years. Many now take the view that if the foreskin cannot be pushed back over the glans soon after birth, it is better to delay thoughts of operation for a few months, until sufficient time has elapsed for a natural separation to have taken place. This nearly always does occur before the end of the first year. As soon as the foreskin will retract easily, push it back every day to cleanse it, and to remove any accumulation of the natural thick white secretion, called smegma. There is no scientific evidence for the belief that circumcision prevents cancer or infection later on in life ; daily cleansing is just as effective.

Milk and welfare foods for baby

When baby's birth is registered (see page 90), the Registrar will issue, as well as the actual Birth Certificate, a special Birth Form, which you will complete and send with the renewal form from your Expectant Mother's Milk Token Book to the local office of the Ministry of

Pensions and National Insurance.   You will then receive a Child's Milk Token Book and card of tokens, enabling you to obtain the following :

Liquid Milk : The tokens can be exchanged for 7 pints weekly at 4d. a pint, and this continues up to the age of 5 years.   While you are breast-feeding baby, you will of course take the milk yourself.

Dried Milk : If baby is bottle-fed the tokens can, if you wish, be used to obtain National Dried Milk instead of liquid milk (see the instructions in the Token Book). This is supplied in 20-oz. tins (each equivalent to 7 pints milk), and costs 2s. 4d. : the basic allowance is 1 tin per week, but additional supplies at the same price are provided as the child's needs increase.

Orange Juice : This costs 5d. a bottle, and can be obtained at any Welfare Foods Distribution Centre.

Cod Liver Oil : This is also obtained from the Welfare Foods Distribution Centre, but is free : a bottle lasts six weeks.

Registration of birth

Your baby's birth must be recorded at the office of the Registrar of Births and Deaths for the District *in which the birth takes place*, and the registration must be made within 42 days of the child's birth (21 days in Scotland).   You will, of course, already have decided on the name (or names) you are going to give your baby, to avoid any last-minute indecision.

It is normally expected that the information will be

given to the Registrar by one of the parents, though in
certain exceptional cases he may be able to accept it from
some other person.   In practice, however, it is found
that the period of 42 days is sufficient to permit one of
of the parents registering.   For the convenience of
parents, it is usual for the Registrar to attend at hospitals
and the larger maternity nursing homes to register births,
but he is under no obligation to do so, and if for any
reason the birth is not registered in this manner, the
parents must visit the office in the ordinary way.

If it is quite impossible for one of the parents to visit
the Register Office for the district where the birth
occurred, a declaration may be made, on payment of a
fee, before any Registrar of Births and Deaths, for trans-
mission to the proper office.

A Birth Certificate may be obtained at the time of
registration, price 3s. 9d., or the new shortened form of
Certificate for 9d.

Also issued by the Registrar are a card to give to the
doctor on whose National Health Service list you want
your baby entered, and the Birth Form already mentioned
in connection with the Child's Milk Token Book.

The Christening

A christening is never just another formality ; it is an
act of dedication on the part of the parents and con-
gregation.   It would be well to read the Christening
Service carefully beforehand, so that you understand fully
the vows and undertakings that will be made.

You will probably want to have the baby christened at the church which you attend, and the details can be arranged with your vicar or minister, or by applying to one of his vergers. The usual age for christening is from three to four months, but any time within the first year is suitable. After that time baby may be inclined to be too active to control easily during the ceremony ! You will have to choose baby's godparents beforehand, of course—two godmothers and one godfather for a girl ; two godfathers and one godmother for a boy, in the Church of England—so that they (or a proxy) will be at the ceremony.

The Christening Party : After the church service you will probably wish to invite members of your family circle and close friends to your home to celebrate the occasion.

Depending on the time of the christening, the celebration could take the form of either a luncheon party or a tea party. If you are single-handed and decide to entertain your friends to lunch, it would be best to arrange a cold meal, which could be left ready prepared. You could of course toast the baby's health in a glass of wine if you wished to do so.

The simpler and more usual entertainment is a tea party, complete with christening cake. It is an informal party, with no prescribed ritual—simply a meeting of family and friends to celebrate a happy occasion. A suitable menu for tea would be : iced rich fruit cake, sandwiches, petits fours, fancy cakes and sponge cake.

The Baby in the Home

During the months before he was born, the baby was sheltered in your body and drew his nourishment directly from you. Once he is born, he must maintain a separate existence, but the tie is not wholly broken and he still depends on you for his very survival. It is in the experience of breast-feeding that the mother and baby are most completely one, and to the baby this is of the most profound importance. His mother nourishes him, satisfies his urgent needs, gives him something to build on in this strange new world, and so forms his first relationship.

It is through the intimate physical tending which you give the baby that he learns of your love and thrives on it. As you hold him in your arms while you feed him, as you wash and change him and attend to his bath, he will begin to respond to you and recognise you as the person who cares for him. You should talk to even a tiny baby ; the words don't matter, but he will listen to the gentle tones of your voice. The end of the baby's day, at the six o'clock feed, is a good time to give a little extra attention and mothering, and if father can get home in time to join in, so much the better.

If baby is a little fretful and there is no evidence that his digestion is worrying him, then he probably needs your presence. We know that a baby should not be constantly disturbed and picked up and that he must have plenty of opportunity for quiet rest, but this can be overdone. Babies are little human beings, and when they are awake, they like to see people round them and to watch the moving leaves of the trees. Don't push the pram right out of sight and hearing and leave the baby to spend hours on his own. Let him see your face and hear children playing near him—he will be all the happier for a little company and some new interests. If he wakes before you are ready to feed him, try uncovering his limbs so that he is free to wave them about vigorously, and he will soon learn to enjoy letting off his energy in this way.

When baby is about a fortnight old, your local Health Visitor will probably call upon you to offer you any help you may require. The Health Visitor is a nurse with special qualifications, whose advice and practical assistance can be invaluable to all mothers, whatever their social status. So do give her the welcome she deserves ! She in turn will be glad to welcome you at the Infant Welfare Centre, and if you are lucky enough to have one within easy reach, you should begin your regular visits as soon as you are up and about. These Centres, which are staffed by Health Visitors and Doctors with a special interest in maternity and infant welfare, are intended to supplement rather than replace the services of your own doctor. As well as supplying advice on the feeding, management and minor ailments of babies, the Centre offers facilities for weighing and recording progress. In many cases baby's orange juice, cod liver oil and National Dried Milk are distributed through the

Centres. There are facilities for test-weighing, should it be necessary, and vaccination and immunisation can be carried out if you wish.

It is always wise to keep a record of your baby's weight, so if the Centre is too far away, remember that it is usually possible to get him weighed at a chemist's ; scales can also be hired from some firms or chemists' shops.

Handling your baby

A baby appreciates feeling snug and secure, and is easily frightened if he feels unsafe. Young though he is, he can sense anxiety and lack of serenity in those who handle him. So if you are not calm and placid by nature, do make a great effort to take things more easily when you are with him ; try to relax and let yourself enjoy him, and be gentle and firm in all things. When you go to pick him up, speak to him first in a low, soft tone, then gently pull away the bedclothes and place your arms well under and around him, so that he is secure before you begin to lift him up. Similarly, when putting him down in his cot, bend down and place your arms in the cot with the baby in them, as it were, then gently take them from under him. Tuck him in firmly and cosily, but see that the covers are not too tight over his legs. When he is very new he will be contented if he is wrapped in a shawl, with his arms at his sides, but as he grows he should have more freedom.

The baby's back and neck muscles are not yet sufficiently strong to support him, and he will not be able to hold his head up until he is about three months, nor to sit up until seven or eight months. So when picking him up and carrying him, make sure that his spine and head are well supported.

Planning the baby's day

It may take up to three weeks to discover what particular feeding schedule will fit in best with your baby's requirements. Some infants may need a feed almost every three hours at first, and one during the night; others will wait quite happily for four hours or so. It is unwise to try to impose a rigid routine upon a baby if it is unsuitable for his particular needs. If he is really hungry, he will never learn to wait for his food until the clock indicates that he can have it. If made to wait too long he will feel frustrated and anxious, which besides making him unhappy, tends to cause frequent stools. Most babies swallow air when they cry, and this is one cause of " windy spasms." But the need to feed more often than three-hourly is very rare if the baby is allowed to take as much as he wants at a feed.

Once the baby's natural routine has been found, you should make every effort to keep to it as far as you are concerned, because he needs the feeling of security which a well-ordered routine gives.

(The above remarks do not apply to a premature or abnormally sleepy baby who, because he cannot indicate his hunger in the usual way, has to be wakened for a feed. But the doctor will advise you in these cases.)

Here are two time-tables, one based on four-hourly feeding and one on three-hourly, which will give you some sort of framework into which you can fit your own baby's routine.

Four-hourly Feeding :	*Three-hourly Feeding :*
6 a.m. Feed and change; return to cot.	6 a.m. Feed and change; return to cot.
9.30 a.m. Bath and kicking time.	8.30 a.m. Bath and kicking time.
10 a.m. Feed ; outdoor sleep in pram.	9 a.m. Feed ; outdoor sleep in pram.
2 p.m. Feed and change; return to pram.	12 noon. Feed and change; return to pram.
5.30 p.m. Mothering time.	3 p.m. Feed and change; lay baby in cot or pram.
6 p.m. " Top-and-tail " wash; feed and sleep in cot.	5.30 p.m. Mothering time.
10 p.m. Feed and change.	6 p.m. " Top-and-tail " wash; feed and sleep in cot.
	10 p.m. Feed and change.

Night feed as and when necessary in either case.

You will probably find that there is one period during the day when baby is more wakeful than at other times, and during which he may be inclined to cry. Use this time to wheel him out shopping, if convenient, or to give him his orange juice, or to mother him, or it may be expedient to bath him then. He will then be able to

B.B.—7

enjoy his waking time, and sleep peacefully for the rest
of the twenty-four hours without being disturbed.

Routine for baby and toddler

It is often a very puzzling problem for the mother
when the second baby arrives before the first has completed his second year, though it is a good thing from
several points of view. The two children grow up side
by side and generally become very good friends. The
mother, however, is sometimes worried as to how she
is going to manage, so here is a daily programme,
arranged so that it causes the least amount of incon-
venience to the little people concerned. You must, of
course, adapt it to your own circumstances and vary it
according to the age of the toddler and the baby's feeding
routine. You may want your toddler to sleep in the
afternoon, and so decide to keep him about during the
morning. Again, when baby is fretful, you may decide
to feed him at 5.30 p.m. before the toddler is bathed.

6.0 a.m.	Baby's first feed, after which baby is changed and put in his cot for a further sleep.
7.45 a.m.	Wash and dress toddler.
8–8.30 a.m.	Breakfast for toddler and grown-ups.
9.30–10.15 a.m.	Bath and feed baby. Toddler plays in playpen or comes to help.
10.15 a.m.	Baby put out in pram for sleep.
10.30 a.m.	Toddler has orange juice and rusk and then goes for his morning sleep in cot or pram.

12.30–1 p.m.	Dinner for toddler and mother.
2 p.m.	Feed baby while toddler plays in playpen.
2.30 p.m.	Baby put outside in pram again. Toddler is put in a second pram or in his cot, with playthings. If too old for second rest, playtime indoors or out. Mother rests for half an hour when possible.
3.30 p.m.	Both children out for a walk.
4.30–5 p.m.	Tea-time for toddler and mother. Baby has orange juice.
5–5.30 p.m.	Combined playtime.
5.30 p.m.	Toddler's bath-time, then bed.
6.0 p.m.	Baby "topped and tailed," fed, and put into his cradle for sleep.
10.0 p.m.	Baby's feed.

You really do need a playpen when dealing with two young children, if you have housework to do as well. A seat to fix on to the pram is also an asset. During the early months baby can often use the " Moses " basket or portable cot, which can be put in the garden, thus reserving the pram for the toddler : this is a very good plan in the summer.

Sleep and exercise

After food, sleep is your baby's greatest physical need. In the first year, particularly, his brain and nervous system are developing at a tremendous rate, and he needs many hours of unbroken sleep to ensure his satisfactory progress. He should never be wakened to be shown off to visitors, however important. If it is really necessary to take him on a journey, try to provide him with a basket or carry-cot, so that he can sleep more comfortably than in your arms. In short, try to interfere as little as possible with his sleeping habits.

Satisfying feeds, firm but gentle handling, peaceful surroundings and sufficient mothering all play their part in ensuring healthy sleep. And both for this purpose and for his physical development he also needs adequate opportunity for exercise, especially as he grows older. Even as a tiny baby he will welcome the chance to kick and wave his arms about, and will enjoy splashing in his bath. A good time to let him kick is just before a feed, if he is awake and not ravenously hungry. In warm surroundings, take his covers off and loosen his clothing, so that his activity is unimpeded. (See page 170 for more suggestions about exercise.)

From about six months onwards he becomes more interested in his surroundings, and needs more company, simple occupations and an occasional change of scenery. You cannot expect him to lie peacefully in his pram all day without occupation or company, and then settle down in his cot in the evening for more sleep all night. Even from a very early age babies enjoy the sound of their mothers' voices talking and singing to them. The afternoon outing has a definite value at this age : it gives him a pleasant sense of movement and fresh surroundings to look at. When he cannot go out because of the weather, provide him with a simple toy or two, such as a rattle or coloured beads.

The actual number of hours of sleep which babies require varies just as their other needs do, but here is a table of " average " hours of sleep which may serve as a guide. There is no need to worry if your particular baby takes less, so long as he is contented and satisfied. The important thing is that he should be given the opportunity to have all that he needs.

Birth to 2 months—about 21 hours of the 24

2 to 4	,,	—19 to 20	,,	,,
4 to 6	,,	—about 19	,,	,,
6 to 12	,,	16 to 17	,,	,,

After he is a year old he will probably dispense with the afternoon sleep altogether ; and if he has a good morning sleep and settles down well after his tea-supper, this is a satisfactory working arrangement.

Causes of disturbed sleep

During the first few weeks

Hunger is the most common cause for crying during the small hours. If you have found by experience that changing his napkin and giving him a small drink of boiled water are not sufficient to help him to settle again, he certainly needs a feed. You cannot train a hungry baby to sleep through the night by ignoring his crying at 2 a.m. He does not understand his mother's motives for leaving him unhappy and unsatisfied ; he only knows that he is hungry, and feels angry and frustrated if food is denied to him. There is no danger that feeding him thus during these few weeks will create a long-standing habit of night feeding, because as the baby gets stronger and takes more nourishment during the day, he will gradually sleep longer and longer during the night, until he goes through until morning. In those babies who need night feeds to start with, this process may take up to eight or ten weeks. Be sure to see that baby is getting enough milk at the last evening feed ; very often a small complement to the breast milk at this time will ensure a longer sleep during the night.

Colic due to " wind " in the bowel may be the cause of disturbed sleep in some young babies, commonly in the evening just when father is at home and mother wants to relax ! The baby draws up his legs, screaming, and is obviously in pain and cannot be ignored. He must be picked up and comforted. (For treatment see page 186–187 in the Minor Ailments chapter.)

Sometimes a baby is not in pain, but just wakeful and bored in the evenings, and will not settle down. It must be remembered that even at an early age he tends to have one period in the twenty-four hours when he is wakeful and needs company and occupation. If it is more convenient for the mother ror baby to have this wakeful period during the afternoon, she may wheel him out then, and give him his bath and " mothering " time before he goes to bed in the evenings.

During the second six months

Other causes of wakefulness may now appear. Some babies just do not need so much sleep as others, and they may lie awake for an hour or so in the night quite happily. So far as the baby is concerned, no treatment is called for, though it may be necessary to make his cot more rigid if he rocks it. If he tends to kick off the bed-clothes, put him to sleep in a large bag with arm-holes, made from one or two thicknesses of blanket and big enough for him to have plenty of room to kick.

But if the baby is unhappy and cries during the night he must not be ignored ; indeed, for the sake of the parents and neighbours, he cannot be ! Here again, hunger may be the cause, and his diet should be recon-sidered. From the age of six or seven months a dinner of broth, strained vegetables and fruit is not sufficient ; he should also have some other form of protein and a little milk pudding. A cereal may be necessary at bed-time, especially if the ten o'clock feed has been omitted.

Teething is a common cause of disturbed sleep at this stage, especially when the molars and canines are coming.

As the teeth push their way through the gums to the surface, considerable discomfort may be caused, at least enough to wake the baby, even though he is soon soothed by his mother's comforting. Other signs of teething are dribbling, biting the fingers and other handy objects, and rubbing the ears. In these cases you can try soothing the gums with a little milk of magnesia rubbed on with your clean finger. But if the disturbance lasts for several nights, consult your doctor about the possibility of giving him a sedative until he is comfortable again.

Another possible cause for waking during this teething period is the scalding of a tender skin by ammonia which may be liberated from the urine. (See "Napkin Rash," pages 193-194, for treatment.)

Some older babies sleep better if they have a small light in the room or shining in from the landing.

Sleep may be disturbed because the baby is too hot, so give him the minimum of blankets to keep him warm. Remember that he is lying on a rubber sheet, which always adds to the warmth of the cot, and that he is in any case a good generator of heat.

Perhaps unhappiness is one of the most common causes of baby crying in the night, and may also be the reason for difficulty in his settling off to sleep. Love and a feeling of security are as essential to a baby as physical nourishment. The personality is developing quickly at this stage, and if there is much conflict over making him take his food or in habit-training, or if he is left alone a great deal when awake, he will be insecure and unhappy. The whole emphasis of his management should be on affectionate encouragement, not rigid discipline and conflict. If he is unhappy when he goes to bed, he will not easily settle down, and when he does fall asleep his unhappiness may remain with him and may wake him from time to time.

Cot-rocking is a habit that is commoner during the second year, so we deal with it in the chapter, "The Growing Baby."

Baby's outings

It is a mistake to think that a tiny baby must be wheeled out in his pram every day. If you have to go

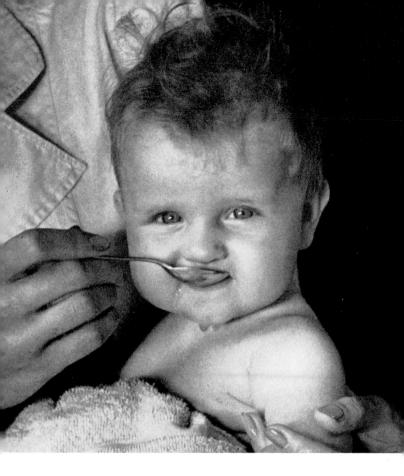

Plate V

BABY CARE AND MANAGEMENT

The pictures on these four pages show how bath-time can be made a joy for both baby and mother. Above : it is a good idea to give baby his cod-liver oil at this time, to avoid getting stains on his clothes.

Plate VI

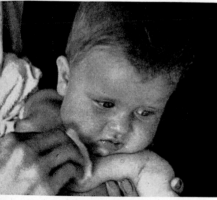

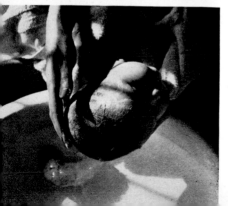

BATH-TIME

Before you begin to bath the baby, see that you have everything you will need within easy reach. Wash baby's face and ears with a soft cloth kept for the purpose. Now make a good lather all over his head, and hold him over the bath to rinse it off. Dry gently but thoroughly. (See chapter " Baby's Layette and Equipment " for bath-time requisites, and " The Baby in the Home " for advice on the bath and the toilet.)

Wash baby's body with your soapy hand, turning him over to soap his back. Rinse him in the bath, grasping him firmly under shoulders and buttocks to lower him into the water. Let him splash a little if he enjoys it, but do not leave him in too long. Lift him out on to a warm soft towel, and dry him immediately, patting rather than rubbing. Apply a little baby cream between the legs, and then powder him lightly.

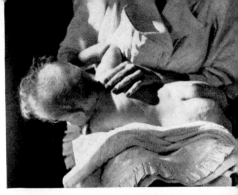

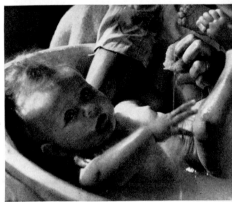

Plate VII

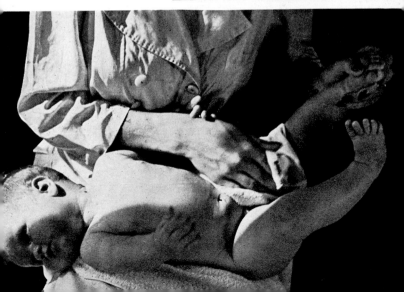

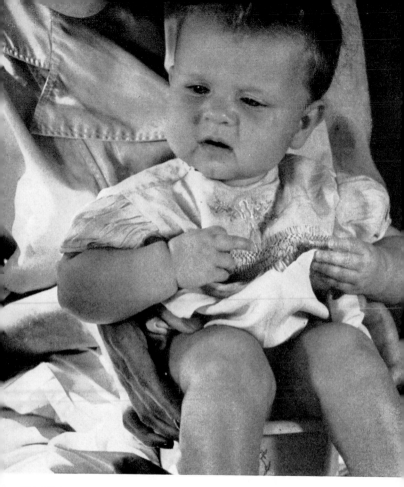

Plate VIII

When baby can sit up, he can be held out
regularly on a pot placed on your lap, though
true habit-training will not start till about the end
of the first year, when he begins to exercise real
control over his functions.

out shopping and cannot leave him asleep in the garden with someone within hearing, then it cannot be helped. But ideally baby should sleep out of doors all day, winter or summer, and the less he is wheeled about the better, until he is old enough to sit up and take notice, which is not usually until six or seven months. The only weather which is really unsuitable for baby is fog. Rain will not harm him at all, if the storm cover on his pram and his hood are up. On cold days put him in his warm pram-suits with feet attached to them, and gloves, too, if possible. If he chews his gloves until they are sodden and cold, make a pair of loose wash-leather bags to cover the woollen ones, and attach them to the sleeves. A bonnet should not be necessary until he is sitting up. Baby can be put out within a few days of his birth.

Sunshine : Everyone knows the value of sunshine to health, but not everyone realises how sensitive a baby's skin is, and how easy it is to burn him with prolonged exposure. So exposure should be gradual, say no more than five minutes at first. (Remember that at the sea-side the reflection of the sun's rays off the sea adds to their intensity.) When he is lying on his back, the eyes of a small baby should never be in the direct sunlight. A pram canopy is a great boon in summer.

Bath-time

Probably you have had at least one practice bath at the hospital or nursing home, or before your nurse left you, and you have realised how very important it is to have everything at hand before actually taking baby on your knee. The clean nappies and day clothes, the bath-time requisites such as soap, sponge, cream, powder, little face-cloth and soft towel—and, if baby is bottle-fed, the ready-prepared bottle standing in a jug of hot water to keep warm—all these things must be laid out within easy reach before you pick baby up, or you will make bath-time uncomfortable and annoying both for yourself and for baby. (See Plates VI and VII.)

Fill your bath with water, a little hotter than the required temperature of 95° F., as it will cool slightly before you are ready to put baby in it. It is a good plan to have a jug of cold water at hand, so that you can adjust the temperature of the water, if necessary, while baby is on your lap. If you have no bath thermometer —and it is not essential—test the water with your elbow. It should feel just slightly warm and certainly not hot or cold. Actually, you will notice that for the first three or four years of his life baby will like his bath much cooler than you would yourself, and you should always err on the side of having the water too cool rather than too warm.

For yourself you will need a soft but waterproof apron. A plastic-backed apron is a very good choice ; failing this you should provide yourself with a flannel one and a waterproof apron to wear underneath it. Over that, you should lay a large, soft towel, warmed if baby is still very tiny or the weather very cold.

When all is ready, take baby on to your knee, if you are going to sit down to the bath, and undress him. If you can spare him a few minutes for a preliminary kick on your knee, free of nappies but otherwise still in his night clothes, he will love the feel of warmth and freedom this provides. Once you begin to undress him, go straight ahead calmly but without delay.

When all his garments are off, wrap him round in the towel and cleanse the eyes and nose. Your little cotton-wool swabs will be ready in a jar beside you ; use a separate clean one for each eye, dipped in boiled water, and gently wiped over the eyelid outward from the inner corner. Two more swabs, dipped in boiled water and pinched to a point, may be needed to cleanse the nostrils, but this only needs to be done if baby's nose is actually dirty.

Next, baby's face and ears are washed, no soap at all being used for the first three months of his life. The cloth should be soft—a piece of gauze napkin will do very well if kept for this purpose. Now soap your right hand until you have a good lather and rub it all over baby's head. To rinse, hold baby so that his head comes over the bath and wash off the soap thoroughly, or scurf may develop. Gently dry the face and head—and now baby is ready to take his bath.

Unwrap the bath towel from his body, and while he still lies in your lap, soap him thoroughly all over with your hand, turning him over to soap the back. Be as quick about this part of the procedure as possible, or he will get cold. The correct hold for lowering baby into the water, so that he feels quite secure and will not slip out of your grasp, is as follows : place one hand right under his shoulder and holding him under his arm, the other firmly grasping his buttocks. Lower him gently into the water and squeeze out the flannel or sponge a few inches above his body so that the water splashes on to it. He will love the feel of this, and even when only a week or so old will relax and try to move his limbs about, and the gentle splashing has a splendid tonic action on the skin. If some sudden noise or movement should cause him to take fright while he is in the bath, grasp his forearms—the left one with your left hand which is already underneath him, the right with your free hand—and hold them still against his chest for a moment or two. This will give him the sense of being securely held which is one of his greatest comforts in life.

Do not keep him in the water longer than a minute or so, but lift out, holding him in the same way as before. Lay him face downwards on your lap, which is already covered with the warm, soft towel, and dry him immediately, wrapping the towel round him as you do so. Dry very thoroughly between the legs, by patting rather than rubbing, using a soft napkin as well as the big towel, and apply a little emollient cream and powder lightly.

Baby powder, though it does make him feel and smell delicious, should be used sparingly, and only one of the finest brands chosen, especially during the early months.

If baby has developed any trace of napkin rash (and however beautifully he is kept it does sometimes happen when the first teething symptoms appear) the inflamed

skin should be very gently patted with a soft napkin
until dry and then a little baby cream applied to soothe
away the soreness. A little dusting of fine baby powder,
on top of the cream, will help to prevent irritation and
incidentally avoid grease-spots on the napkins. (For
treatment of napkin rash, see pages 193–194.)

The change-over to an evening bath : You will find that
as soon as baby begins to crawl—that is, any time after
nine months—he will get so grubby, particularly about
the hands and knees, that he will need a good clean up
before going to bed. This is the time to change over
from the morning to the evening for the bath—say, at
about 5.30, to give him time to digest his tea. If he
requires supper, a drink of warm milk can be given after
the bath. In the morning sponge him all over with warm
water before dressing him.

At this stage, too, he may get so vigorous that he
splashes a lot of water about. His little bath may be
placed in the big bath, if necessary, during the month or
two that may elapse before he can sit up in the big bath.

Baby's napkins

While baby is still very tiny, the regulation allowance
of napkins—one thick and one thin—does seem to make
a tremendous pad between the legs. On the other hand,
the thickness is definitely needed to soak up the moisture.
A very good compromise is effected by pinning the thin
napkin in the ordinary three-corner position, but wrapping the thick one round the body like a skirt, fastening
it with one or two pins.

As he grows bigger you will need to use both the thin and the thick variety of napkins.

Here are two methods of putting on nappies :—

The Triangular Method

This method is suitable before the baby begins to sit up. The nappy is folded diagonally so that it is triangular in shape and of double thickness.

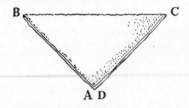

Make sure that baby's buttocks are clean and dry, and then lay him on the nappy. Fold points B and C round his body so that they cross over in front of his tummy, bring the points labelled AD up between his legs, and fasten with a safety-pin.

The Pilch Method

This method can be adopted as being less bulky when the baby becomes more active. Fold the napkin in two, so that it is oblong in shape.

Prepare baby as in first method and then lay him on the nappy ; the upper part should well cover his buttocks. Draw the lower part up between his legs and fasten at each side, using two safety-pins, so that F lies over E and CD lies over AB.

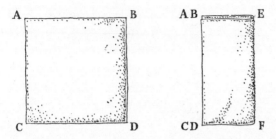

Changing the nappies : The napkins should be changed at least five times during the day for a four-hourly-fed baby, or six times for a three-hourly-fed one (i.e. at every feed time). If baby soils his napkins between times, you will naturally give him the comfort of clean ones immediately, and it is surprising how soon the tiniest mite can make you aware that he is uncomfortable.

If baby is wet when you pick him up to feed him, remove the wet napkin and lay him on a dry one while he is feeding. Then you can " pot " him after the feed and pin on the nappy, being very gentle in the process, or you may make him sick and undo all the good you have done him with the meal.

Washing the nappies : If you have followed the advice on page 59, and always put a pad of cellulose wadding inside the gauze napkin, you should rarely have a soiled napkin to wash—and as it is the stained napkins that need most care to keep them white, you will thus reduce the heavy washing a good deal.

Here is a routine which will save precious moments each day. Every time you change baby, destroy the soiled wadding, put the two wet napkins into a pail of plain cold water (keep the pail handy and covered with a lid) and leave them to soak until you are ready to wash them. Pure soap flakes or a mild soapless detergent, mixed to a lather with warm water, should be used for the washing. The rinsing is very important, and at least two lots of clean water should be used. Napkins dried in the open air will keep their colour beautifully, but if you have to dry them indoors, and later, when teething may indirectly cause yellow staining of nappies, regular boiling is important; this also, of course, sterilises the napkins. Alternatively, you may like to follow the " Milton routine," as described on the bottles.

If you use a washing-machine, follow the maker's directions regarding washing products, etc.

For indoor drying it is convenient to have a rack which lets down from the ceiling, if possible fixed above the kitchen boiler or stove. In this way napkins, and woollens, too, will dry over-night and can then finish off in the airing cupboard.

Laundering baby's woollies

Use soap flakes or a mild soapless detergent (one specially prepared for woollies is now made), with water as hot as your hands can comfortably bear. Rinse thoroughly in water of the same temperature as the washing water— one of the most important points in washing woollies.

In hard-water districts, soapless detergents are good for washing woollies because they do not react with hard water to form lime curd. If you use soap flakes, soften

the water with Calgon water-softening powder : about
1 tbsp. to 10 gallons for London water.

To avoid matting and shrinkage, take care never to rub
woollies—squeeze instead, and rinse two or three times
in clear water. Remove the excess moisture by rolling
the garment up in an absorbent towel. Dry at once,
preferably out of doors, but not in direct sun, which
will discolour wool, turning your white woollies yellow.

For cod-liver oil stains on baby's woollies or other
clothes, apply a grease solvent, such as carbon tetrachlo-
ride or a new jelly type grease solvent which is very easy
to use ; then wash the garment in warm soapy water.
If the stain is very persistent, bleach with a solution
of hydrogen peroxide (1 part in 5 parts of water) and a
few drops of ammonia, afterwards rinsing thoroughly.

Some baby wool stretches when wet, so take care not to
hang the garment up carelessly. Ideally it should be laid
out flat to preserve the shape. If there is any tendency to
shrink, gently pull the wet garment to its original shape.

If you dry woollies flat, whether on a special drying
hammock or any other clean surface, be sure that the
air can circulate freely below and around them.

It adds to the appearance of matinee coats and other
tiny garments if they are lightly pressed while still slightly
damp. Use a cool iron and work carefully, pressing the
garment back into shape if it should have become slightly
distorted. Avoid pressing any ribbing, and iron lightly
over patterns. Other woollies do not need ironing at
all, though ribbons can be pressed out if required.

All woollies should be very thoroughly aired.

B.B.—8

Habit training

The important thing to remember about toilet training is that it is not simply a matter of building up a good physical habit—baby's feelings are involved in it. His earliest experiences come to him through his bodily processes, and healthy elimination is a natural source of satisfaction to him.

It is advisable to leave him undisturbed for the first few months, then to begin to hold him out regularly for a few minutes in a quiet, gentle way, as part of the daily routine, to accustom him to the use of the pot. He may oblige then, but as long as his food is mainly liquid, he cannot be expected to remain dry for long, and the whole matter should be treated without fuss. It is not until near the end of the first year that the baby begins to exercise any real muscular control over his eliminations, and that true habit-training begins.

Start then by holding him out on his pot when he first wakes in the morning, before and after meals, and before and after being put down to sleep. You may be fortunate enough to win his co-operation readily, and training proceeds steadily. Don't be surprised or anxious, however, if baby goes through a phase, which may last throughout his second year, when he shows a great dislike for his pot. The best way to proceed is to discard nappies during the time he is awake, and to substitute for them absorbent pilch-type knickers. Teach the baby a little sound or word to say to indicate his need. Gradually, if the pace is not forced, he will report to you after he has performed, and when you change him you can show him the pot. As his confidence and his muscular control improve he will learn to tell you what he needs before the accident has happened. If he strongly rejects the pot don't force him, but wait for a week, then quietly offer it again. Please don't feel that your baby is never going to be clean because he seems to be taking a long time ; the phase will pass, and when it is over you will wonder why you worried so much.

Bladder control during the night may not be achieved until many months later than day-time control. When the 10 p.m. feed is dropped, it is customary to continue to pot the baby at this time. If he accepts the routine easily and settles down again quickly, it is useful to adopt it, but if he becomes thoroughly disturbed and remains awake, it is better to leave him to sleep, and to wait until he can naturally keep dry all night. You should always try, however, to offer him the pot as soon as he wakes.

Many mothers worry unduly over comparisons with other babies in the matter of toilet training. Remember that a baby who is trained gradually at his own pace is likely to be more serene and less likely to have set-backs later on than one who is hurried in this respect.

Baby's toilet

Care of the nails : You will find that baby's nails grow quickly, and that he easily scratches his face if they are not cut. Therefore cut them carefully whenever they begin to protrude beyond the finger-tips, using a small, fine pair of scissors. If necessary, do it while he is asleep.

Cutting baby's hair : Usually round about the age of nine–twelve months baby's hair becomes straggling and rather inclined to look untidy. It is at this stage that a first professional hair-cut can be of great assistance. Proper cutting of the hair stimulates healthy growth, and it is therefore usually best to get a hairdresser to do the job. Once the hair has been cut the growth tends to be more even, and a second hair-cut will not be needed for some months.

Care of the teeth : As soon as the baby has three or four teeth, it is a good plan to start to clean them with a very soft toothbrush and boiled water. But be very gentle and make a game of it, otherwise you may make the child dislike the whole process. In fact, if he does object strongly at first, it is better to put off the tooth-brush drill until later. Chewing hard rusks, raw apple and carrot, helps the development of the teeth and gums ; the apple and carrot also have a cleansing effect. Remains of soft, sweet food in the teeth probably encourage decay, and as the child grows older it is wise to start the habit of rinsing the mouth with water after eating a sweet or other sweet food. But in any case, see that the baby's teeth are clean before he goes to sleep at night.

The normal thumb-sucking of infants does no harm to the teeth.

If you notice any discoloration or abnormality of the teeth, see your dentist. It is important to preserve the milk teeth, because they keep the necessary space in the gum for the permanent ones later on.

The baby's feet : The good body- and bone-building

foods—milk, eggs, cheese, butter, cod liver oil and green vegetables—which you are giving to your baby will all help to build up strong feet with good bones.

The baby should have plenty of opportunity to exercise the muscles of his feet, which hold the bones in correct position. Leave his feet bare as much as possible, and let him kick in his pram, or against your hand to strengthen his muscles. Give him freedom of movement, but don't hurry his walking, especially if he is a heavy baby.

When he first gets on to his feet, still allow him to go barefoot wherever he safely can. If he can grip the ground with his toes he will develop a light, springy walk, and will develop the muscles of his feet.

The feet must, of course, be washed regularly, and they must be dried very thoroughly, especially between the toes, otherwise the skin will become soft and sodden.

Socks and shoes : It is important that a baby or growing child should never wear socks which are too tight. He will soon let you know if his shoes pinch him, but will probably say nothing about tight socks, yet socks that are too small can soon do damage to a soft foot, by making the toes curl under, thus losing the natural straight line from the point of the big toe to the heel. If the feet are to be firm and healthy, the socks should be changed frequently.

When the baby can walk, but not before, buy him some well-fitting shoes. Always take him with you, as feet vary so much in proportions that it is almost impossible to buy the right fitting by just quoting the length, particularly if your baby happens to have rather chubby feet. Laced shoes give better support than strap sandals, and the ankle-strap type in particular should be avoided for small children. The shoes should be decidedly longer than baby's feet. Points to look for are that the shoes should be flexible and waterproof; they should be wide at the toes, and fit firmly at the heel and instep.

But shoes need only be worn when conditions are unsuitable for the baby to be bare-footed. The more he is free to use his foot muscles, the better.

Premature babies

The care and management of a premature baby (that is, one whose birth weight is $5\frac{1}{2}$ lb. or less) should always be under the direction of a doctor. To begin with, the baby requires warmth and an even temperature, and above all he should be protected from any infection. It is surprising how well these small babies then progress.

Your doctor or Welfare Clinic will give you details of how to borrow any necessary special equipment.

The care of twins

If you should have to provide for twins, you will need nearly, but not quite, twice the amount of clothes and equipment as for a single baby. Your plans will be influenced to some extent by the amount of space you have for equipment, and also by the help which you will have. Certainly you will want to keep the number of clothes down to a reasonable minimum, but on the other hand you will be glad of a small reserve for those days when you cannot get enough clean clothes ready for the next day. You should be able to manage with 8 gowns, 6 vests and 4 matinee coats for the two babies. Don't economise on napkins, however.

Good laundry facilities are very important where there are twins : a washing-machine and, if possible, an electric drying-cabinet are a real boon—you will need all the labour-saving devices you can possibly get.

Equipment : Each baby will need his own cot—either a wicker cradle or a carry-cot. Probably one of them could be borrowed from a friend. At about six months they will need separate drop-side cots.

It is best for the babies to sleep separately when in the garden, as they would begin to disturb each other as soon as they grew more active. For the first few months you could put one to sleep in the twin pram (which you would need when you took them out together), while the second baby used a carry-cot on a stand with hood and apron. Later on, a twin push-chair can be used.

Breast feeding of twins : Many mothers find they have sufficient milk to feed twins for at least three months. Ideally, each baby should be fed separately, but in many homes where the mother is single-handed, there is not usually time for this, and with practice it can become quite easy to feed them together. One method is to put each baby on a pillow or cushion, head towards the mother and feet underneath her arms. Alternatively, have one baby lying partially on top of the other, legs pointing in the same direction, so that both babies are supported by one arm, your other hand being free to regulate the flow of milk when necessary.

If the supply of milk is not so plentiful, give the children alternate breast and bottle feeds. For example:—

Child A : Give breast feeds at 6 a.m., 2 p.m. and 10 p.m., with bottle feeds at 10 a.m. and 6 p.m. *Child B :* Bottle feeds at 6 a.m., 2 p.m. and 10 p.m., with breast feeds at 10 a.m. and 6 p.m. On the following day, reverse the time-tables.

In cases of real difficulty—if, for instance, one baby is not thriving—it may be necessary to breast-feed that child completely, and bottle-feed the other.

Bottle-feeding of twins : If you are single-handed, it is possible to give both babies their bottle feeds at the same time. Put the babies on cushions, one in each corner of an arm-chair, stand behind the chair, and lean over, holding both bottles. Alternatively, lay the babies side by side at one end of a settee, seat yourself at the other end and hold both bottles ; one arm supported on the back of the settee will help to take your weight.

Feeding twins at weaning time : You will probably find it easiest to let both babies sit in their high chairs or buffers. You can then stand or sit facing them and feed both at the same time, a spoon in each hand (you will, of course, have to train yourself to use your left hand as much as your right). Babies soon become accustomed to the procedure of being fed together, and if they are always on the same side of you, they get used to the angle of the spoon. It is even possible—with practice— to give them drinks at the same time.

Travelling with a Baby

If you are taking a baby on a journey, the simplest one to arrange is by car. A young baby can travel comfortably in a carry-cot or wicker cradle, placed on the back seat. For those who expect to travel often by car, it would be a good idea to invest in a pram with a detachable body ; the body can be used as a carry-cot and the chassis stored in the luggage boot. For a small toddler you can buy a car seat which keeps him safely and comfortably in place.

For use on any long journey, you can make a linen hold-all, divided into ample pockets by rows of machine stitches, and pin it on to the back of the front seat—it will hold a bottle of orange juice, a spare hand towel, clean nappies, plastic bag for wet nappies, and any other immediate necessities.

Travelling by train, with its greater restrictions, needs more careful thinking out. If your baby is breast-fed, try to arrange to feed him just before you leave home, or make use of one of the several partitions of the ladies' rooms provided at most of the big stations. Where there is a First Aid room in the station, the nurse in charge may well give you permission to nurse your baby there. Do your best to choose a corridor train. On occasions when he must be fed on the train, surely the most sensible thing to do is to consider the baby's well-being first and quietly carry on, with the baby's shawl to screen you.

An artificially fed or weaned baby needs more detailed provision, and suggestions are given in the paragraph

"Feeds During Travelling," on page 159. Remember that small children are more likely to be thirsty than hungry on journeys : a supply of orange juice, carried in a bottle or flask, will be a help. Use a good covering feeder with sleeves when you are giving the baby his dinner. If there is a restaurant car in your end of the train, you can usually obtain hot water—or milk for older children.

Disposable nappies for babies are a great boon for either single-day travel or for sea journeys. For slightly older children who are not yet able to manage the toilet seat on the train, one solution is to take a collapsible chamber-pot which is easily packed in your luggage.

Air travel with babies and young children presents few problems. A baby can travel in a carry-cot, which is not considered as extra luggage, and cots will usually be provided at the hotels where you stay for the night en route. Air hostesses will help in the preparation of feeds and will do everything possible to make the journey comfortable for young travellers.

If you are taking a baby on a long sea journey, you should enquire beforehand what facilities there are on board for laundry and for help in caring for children on board. As far as possible, dress the children in clothes which can be quickly dried and need no ironing. Where a short journey is in question, try to book a berth.

Babies are usually good travellers and are generally soothed by the movement of train or car. Small toddlers, however, tend to become restless if their movement is restricted for too long. When you are travelling by car, you should plan to make a short break every hour, so that the children can stretch their legs and to have a long lunch-hour, during which the small people can have a real rest.

An understanding grown-up can ease a train journey wonderfully for a very young traveller. Talk to him about the passing scene, show him pictures in a picture book, make him folded paper toys, let him play with a bunch of keys or even a handkerchief knotted into a doll, or play finger games with him. The time will pass much more pleasantly than if you try to impress an unnatural quietness on him. Remember to take the child's favourite toy.

Always provide enough to drink for small children (they feel thirsty far more than hungry on a journey), and have a bottle of cleansing milk and paper tissues at hand for cleaning smutty and sticky hands and faces.

If your baby or toddler is one of the unfortunate few who are liable to travel sickness, ask your doctor if he can suggest pills for combating it.

The working mother

Until a child begins school, he needs the constant daily presence of his mother. But unalterable circumstances do sometimes occur in which the mother must work away from home. If she cannot leave her baby in charge of a full-time deputy in her own home, she can, if circumstances make her eligible (and if there is a vacancy), take him to a day nursery while she is working.

In this case, she needs to make a special effort to compensate him for the changes in his handling. Her life will be a busy one, but when she brings the baby home from the nursery, he has first claim on her attention until he is put to bed. She should keep in the closest possible touch with the staff of the nursery, so that she moves in step with them in ordering the baby's routine. She will want to know, for instance, what is the nursery's attitude to toilet training, just what food is being given at each stage and how long her baby is sleeping during the day, so that there is as little difference as possible between the baby's life at the week-ends and during the week.

Baby-sitters

It may make a great difference to your social life when you find yourself no longer free to go out with your husband in the evenings. No doubt you will accept your new way of life readily enough, but it would be a mistake to feel that you can never have a free evening together.

In most districts it is possible to arrange for someone to sit with your baby in the evenings from time to time, either a student or an older woman, or the local W.V.S. may organise a service. If you want your sitter-in to put the baby to bed or give him his bottle, you should arrange for her to come early on the first occasion and get to know him and his routine before you leave.

Breast-feeding

There is no doubt that breast-feeding can, and should be a very satisfying experience for both baby and mother. It continues the process started in the womb, where baby derives all his nourishment from the mother's blood-stream, and it establishes a close link between mother and child which nothing else can quite replace.

There are other considerations, too. The composition of the milk is just right for baby's needs ; its quantity may vary, but its quality very rarely alters. It is just the right temperature for him ; it is, of course, germ-free, and it costs nothing. But these are secondary points compared with the value of the emotional relationship which is built up. The mother's attitude can have a profound effect upon her baby. The child who is fed by a serenely happy mother will rarely have digestive troubles and will have emotional security in which to develop his personality in the best way. But if the atmosphere in which he is fed is tense and anxious, he will react in the same way, to the detriment of both his digestion and his personality.

It is the regular sucking on baby's part which brings in and establishes the milk supply. Rest for the mother, and an ample diet with plenty of fluids, also help, but the stimulation given by baby's sucking is essential.

Baby should, therefore, be allowed to suck regularly. At the very beginning the " feed " will not be long, as it would cause sore nipples if baby were allowed to suck for more than five minutes at each breast before the milk has come in, on the third or fourth day. Mother will soon learn to recognise when there is milk for baby, and very often after baby has been sucking for half a minute or so she will feel a tingling sensation in the breasts, accompanied by the sense that they are becoming fuller and heavier. Later, when the milk is more plentiful, it is quite usual to feel it coming in about half-way between feeding times.

When the milk is well established there is sometimes a tendency to leakage, especially during feed-times, from the breast which is not being used. A pad of cotton-wool inside the brassière will absorb this, and is quite safe to use if changed after each feed.

During the first five to seven days it is usual for baby to lose a little weight. This is because the milk does not begin to come into the breasts in any large amount until the third or fourth day. Before this there is a thin, watery fluid, called colostrum, in the breast. This is baby's first natural " food " and helps him while his digestive organs are learning to function.

Mothers of more than one child may find with their second or third that there is quite a lot of milk by the second day, and that baby scarcely loses any weight during this waiting time.

Times of feeding

It is quite usual to let the mother have a rest before giving her the baby to feed for the first time, and where labour has been difficult this is particularly important. Baby will probably be fed eight-hourly during the first day, six-hourly during the second day, four-hourly during the third day. If he is small, i.e., less than seven pounds, he will probably need three-hourly feeds on the fourth day, and continue these until he has gained weight and well passed the seven-pound margin. Should he be over seven pounds at birth, it may be decided to keep him on four-hourly feeding right from the first, if that suits him.

Four-hourly feeding, as stated in the time-table on page 97, is generally timed for approximately 6 a.m., 10 a.m., 2 p.m., 6 p.m., and 10 p.m., and three-hourly feeding at 6 a.m., 9 a.m., 12 noon, 3 p.m., 6 p.m., and 10 p.m. During the lying-in period these hours are usually kept, but when you get into your stride again and have the house to run, and a husband and perhaps other children to look after, you may have to change the hours. Even so, it is best to keep to the regular intervals which suit your baby. There is no reason why, if baby sleeps till 7 a.m., the four-hourly intervals should not be reckoned from 7 a.m. Mothers often find that they cannot stick to the exact routine, and if so, it is best not to worry; babies brought up exactly to the clock do not necessarily behave or thrive better than those who are allowed a little latitude.

Baby may find it difficult to sleep right through the night at first. If he does wake, leave him for a few minutes to see if he will settle off; if he does not, change him and put him back in a warmed cot on his other side. If he is still unhappy, do not hesitate to feed him, but give him only as much as will satisfy him. Do not be afraid of creating a habit which will be difficult to break ; for that matter, if you let him cry, you may be in as much danger of creating a habit of crying during the night. Night feeding is now quite usual during the first six or eight weeks. By the end of that period baby is usually taking more nourishment during the day, and is sleeping longer and longer during the night, until the time for waking becomes about 5 a.m., and the feed given at that time can be counted as the first of the day.

Method of breast-feeding

The first essential is that both mother and baby should be comfortable during this time. Some mothers lie in a half-way sitting position, turning slightly on to the side from which baby is going to have his feed. Baby lies on a soft pillow with his head in the curve of his mother's arm. Other mothers like to sit bolt upright, baby being supported on a cushion or pillow which lies across their knees. Some mothers lie flat, turning on to the appropriate side as baby is fed ; baby then lies on the bed beside them. This position, though not so common, gives the mother a good rest, and also comforts baby if his gums are tender, because in this way there is no weight on his gums. But whatever position you do adopt, make yourself comfortable and relaxed before you begin, as these may be the only opportunities you will be able to have during the day.

Whatever position you adopt, you will need to support the lower part of the breast with the little and ring finger of the hand that is not holding baby, i.e., the right hand when baby is on the left breast, and then *vice versa*. The fingers will be placed above and below the nipple, and by approximating them to each other the flow of milk can be somewhat controlled. (See Plate X.)

Before the feed, the hands should be well washed and the nipple should be cleansed with a little boiled water, and afterwards the nipple is again cleansed, and thoroughly dried.

Although baby may get enough milk from one breast only to start with, it is wisest to use both at each feed, for the sake of maintaining the milk supply. Let him start with alternate breasts, because the first is always emptied more completely. Afterwards express what is left, if any.

How long should a feed last? The answer to this in most cases is, " Until baby is satisfied." In practice this works out at about 10 minutes at each breast during the first weeks. Later, as he grows bigger and sucks more strongly, the time may be reduced to about 5 minutes at each side. If he is not satisfied after 20 minutes, you should consider the question of whether your supplies are adequate or not. (See " Underfeeding," page 138.) When there is no more milk left, he will only make your nipple sore and fill himself up with wind, if he continues to suck.

Bringing up wind : It is customary to give a baby a breathing space after the first 5 or 10 minutes, so that

B.B.—9

he has the opportunity of bringing up some wind if he needs to. If you have any difficulty in drawing him away from the nipple, you may find it useful to employ the old trick of inserting your finger into the corner of his mouth to break the vacuum. Then sit him up leaning slightly forward, with one of your hands supporting his back and the other against his tummy. Wait until he belches up the wind, then start him off on the other breast. At the end of the feed sit him up again and be prepared to spend some minutes quietly waiting for him to bring up two or three good belches : the more relaxed he is the better they will come. Sometimes mothers find that it helps the baby to belch if he is held up to the shoulder, with his tummy pressed against the top part of the chest. Many babies return some of their feed with the wind, and so the shoulder must be protected against these possets ! (See Plate X.) Bringing up this wind is an important matter, because it has been shown by X-ray photographs that every time a baby takes a drink of milk or water, he swallows air at the same time. If this is allowed to remain in the stomach, it usually causes discomfort and may wake him from sleep. Even if baby is sleepy, do not be tempted to put him straight down. Just sit him up, well supported, and wait ; as we said before, the more relaxed he is, the easier will the process be.

Many mothers are in the habit of giving baby a bottle of boiled water between feeds. If he is allowed to suck this lying in his pram or cot, the whole purpose is defeated, because the wind is never broken and baby, although he may sleep for a little time, will wake once more crying with pain. If baby does need some boiled water—as he may very well do, especially when teething or during the hot weather—give it to him in a spoon.

Baby's part in breast-feeding : The great majority of babies suck well and lustily, once they have overcome the difficulties of birth, and it is this sucking action on the nipple which helps greatly in bringing in the milk. See that he gets his jaws well behind the nipple, otherwise the milk is not so easily obtained, and the nipple tends to get sore with his increased efforts to get sufficient nourishment.

Do not forget to make baby as comfortable as possible for the feed. If he is very wet, change his nappy, and allow him some freedom of movement for his legs. For the first two months or so it is best to keep him in his shawl during feeds, so that his arms are not free. A muslin nappy or towel placed under his chin will help to protect his clothing. Later, when he has more control over the movements of his arms and hands, they can be left free if desired, and it will often be found that baby likes to hold the breast while he is feeding.

Amounts of milk needed by baby

It has been found by experiment that baby requires about $2\frac{1}{2}$ ounces of milk per pound of body weight each day. Thus, if baby weighs 8 lb., he will require at least 8 times $2\frac{1}{2}$ ounces per day, which is 20 ounces. If he is fed five times a day, that means 4 ounces per feed. Possibly yours will be a " hungry " baby, however, and need rather more than the minimum 20 ounces; you will be wise to allow him some latitude in this respect as in others, and let him have as much as he wants.

Baby will not get his food absolutely evenly during the day, and if he is weighed before and after each feed it will probably be found that the amounts taken are somewhat like this :—

6 a.m.—$5\frac{1}{2}$ ozs.   10 a.m.—$3\frac{1}{2}$ ozs.

2 p.m.—$4\frac{1}{2}$ ozs.   6 p.m.—$3\frac{1}{2}$ ozs.   10 p.m.—3 ozs.

The baby usually takes the smallest feed at 10 p.m., but if he can be persuaded to take more at that time he is more likely to sleep undisturbed through the night and ensure a peaceful rest for the whole household. It will be seen that, in cases where underfeeding is suspected, and to discover how much the baby is actually having, it is necessary to weigh before and after every feed for the whole twenty-four hours, and take a total, rather than the amount of one feed only, as a guide.

This weighing immediately before a feed and immediately after it is called " test weighing." It is not strictly necessary to do this unless you have a reason to believe that baby is not getting enough milk, but many inexperienced mothers are glad of the " sure " feeling it gives. Welfare Centres will arrange for it to be done if the doctor recommends it. Or you may, if you wish, hire a pair of baby scales, as already suggested.

Signs of healthy progress

Baby's progress can be judged in several different ways. His *limbs* are firm and rounded, with no loose folds of

skin. The "*soft spot*" on the top of his head is flush
with the rest of the skull, and neither sinks in nor bulges ;
it progressively becomes smaller, and is usually closed
before the age of eighteen months. He is *alert* and re-
sponsive to attention, and his eyes are bright. He likes
to move his limbs about and to splash in his bath. The
colour of his lips is bright red, even though his cheeks
may be pale. His *sleep* is peaceful and adequate for his
needs, and when he is awake he is usually content. *He
gains weight steadily.* At first baby may be weighed
every two or three days, or even oftener, depending
upon the practice in the hospital or nursing home or of
your maternity nurse. When you are left on your own,
a weekly weighing is ideal, but not absolutely essential
except in special cases. Growth does not take place quite
evenly, so there may be slight variations week by week
in the gains. It is only when they have been consistently
small for two or three weeks that the possibility of underfeeding or of another cause needs to be considered.
After the first three months, the weighing can be once
a fortnight or even once a month, so long as the baby
is progressing normally in other ways. (See "The
Growing Baby" chapter, pages 174–178.)

The character and frequency of the *stools* also give
valuable information about progress. At first, as already
mentioned, they are very dark and tarry in character,
but they soon change colour to bright mustard after a
few days. At this time they are very fluid and frequent,
possibly as many as 12 motions a day. They are sometimes green, and may occasionally contain curds. But

after 6 or 8 weeks they settle down to one or two a day, or less.

As baby grows older, the motions become more formed and the number may be reduced to one a day, or even less. Mothers are apt to fly to magnesia or some similar mild aperient if baby happens to miss a day, and yet in a breast-fed baby it is quite common and normal to have a motion only on every second or even third day. If your baby does behave like this, it probably means he is receiving only just enough milk for his body needs, and breast-milk being the true food it is, this allows no waste at all. If baby's motions are hard and he has a struggle to pass them, it is usually an indication that he is getting too little food or fluid, especially if it is hot weather. Until the necessary adjustments in the diet have improved matters, you may give a teaspoonful of liquid paraffin twice a day to make the motion soft.

Early difficulties with breast-feeding

These difficulties may be due to various conditions in either the mother or the baby, but much can usually be done to improve matters.

The lazy baby : If baby is very much underweight or was a good deal overweight at birth, he is likely to be sleepy and rather difficult to feed. In the case of the overweight baby, it does not do him any harm to lose weight. But the tiny baby must be safeguarded by frequent small feeds, whether he appears to want it or not. Your doctor will give you specific advice on this point. Baby may not suck well, and it will be necessary to empty the breast by hand expression after he has done his best, and then give him more from a pipette. It is very important that at least one breast should be emptied at each feed, as this provides the stimulus necessary to establish the milk supply.

Baby may take well for a few minutes and then fall asleep. If this happens, sit him up and get all the wind up, and start off again. It may be necessary to wake him more forcibly. There is quite a knack in getting the nipple into baby's mouth, especially if he is inclined to let his tongue rest against the roof of his mouth. If he does this, of course, he cannot suck. You will probably have to depress his chin with your finger.

The hungry baby : In this case the baby is so hungry that he has already gulped down a lot of air, and when he starts to feed, he gulps his milk down too quickly, with more air. This all tends to produce " windy spasms," with some possetting of milk after the feed. The remedy is the simple one of feeding him when he is hungry, if milk supplies are good, or of giving complementary feeds if it is suspected that there is less breast milk than before.

Tongue tie : This also hinders sucking if it is at all marked. The doctor can put the condition right if it should be present, but it is not very common.

Shock or exhaustion following a difficult birth often hinders baby's power of suction until it is past. In these cases your doctor will advise you about the best procedure.

Conditions of the breast or nipple which affect feeding :
The nipple may be flat, or even drawn in. If you have
been wise you will have drawn it out during the ante-
natal period as described on page 31, but even when
every precaution has been taken, these nipples are often
found to be tender and difficult for baby to hold.

Draw the nipple gently out before you offer it to
baby, using either massage with your fingers, or gentle
suction with a breast pump. The use of a nipple shield
may be necessary for a week or two until the nipple
becomes more prominent. If, after all these efforts, it
will not stand out sufficiently prominent for the baby to
grasp, attempts to feed from this breast will have to be
abandoned. If the other nipple is good you may be
able to feed the baby from that other breast and give
the milk expressed from the breast with the poor nipple
by spoon or bottle.

Over-distension of the breast may adversely affect the
prominence of the nipple, so that the baby cannot
grasp it properly. In this condition, too, the milk may
come so quickly that the baby is almost drowned in it
and has to gulp to keep pace with the flow, and he is
apt to swallow too much air. The expression of some of
the milk by hand just before a feed will usually overcome
this difficulty. In some rare cases partial suppression of
the milk supply for a time may have to be considered,
and if so, your doctor will prescribe as necessary.

Always support the breast from below as you feed
baby, so that the lower half is emptied as well as the
upper.   When you think baby has finished, gently

PLATE IX

1 (*below*). Lie flat with legs on a stool. Bend feet forward and back from ankle (five times each).

3. Raise and lower the arms, breathing deeply (5 times).

EXERCISES FOR THE WAITING TIME

ove). Fling arms from position ; return to first on (five times).

wist body ight; then left as far possible ir times).

6 (*below*). Get down on hands and knees, resting head on folded arms. Do this three or four times a day.

5 (*on left*). Breathing exercise, keeping abdomen flat, as shown (five times).

BREAST-FEEDING

It is a matter of personal preference whether the mother lies down or sits up to feed her baby; the important point is that both are comfortable. Support the breast with the free hand, the fingers controlling the flow of milk. Half-way through and at the end of the feed, baby should be helped to get up his wind. Either sit him on your lap and rock him slightly from side to side, or hold him up to your shoulder. (See below.)

Plate X

BOTTLE-FEEDING

Hold baby comfortably in your arms while you are feeding him, and tilt the bottle so that the teat is kept full of milk. (Enlarge the hole in the teat with a red-hot needle, if necessary.) Stop half-way through the feed, to let baby bring up wind. When making up the feeds, measure the dried milk accurately, levelling it off with a knife. Clean the bottles with a brush—for upright bottles, use one with a tufted end.

XI

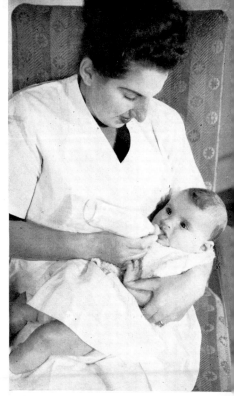

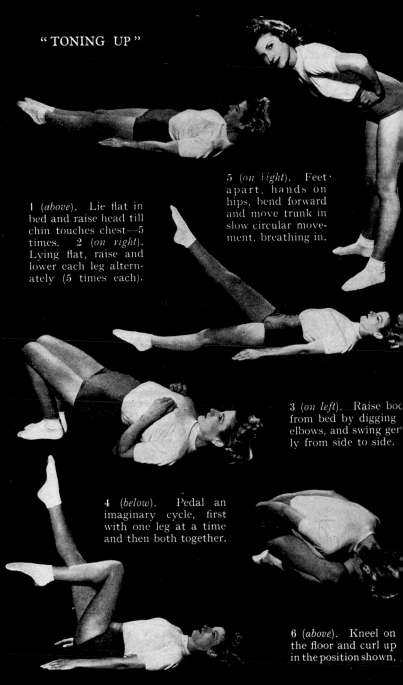

" TONING UP "

1 (*above*). Lie flat in bed and raise head till chin touches chest—5 times. 2 (*on right*). Lying flat, raise and lower each leg alternately (5 times each).

5 (*on right*). Feet apart, hands on hips, bend forward and move trunk in slow circular movement, breathing in.

3 (*on left*). Raise body from bed by digging elbows, and swing gently from side to side.

4 (*below*). Pedal an imaginary cycle, first with one leg at a time and then both together.

6 (*above*). Kneel on the floor and curl up in the position shown.

squeeze the breast and see if there is any milk left. You will soon be able to judge by the feel whether baby has emptied it or not.

Should the breast feel tender or lumpy at any place, relief is often obtained by gently pressing this particular spot as baby feeds, so ensuring that this section of the breast is well emptied.

Infection of nipple or breast : If the nipple becomes sore and cracked, or any redness or very tender patches develop on the breast, be sure to point out the trouble to your doctor or midwife, as all these conditions need immediate treatment, probably in the form of the quick-acting anti-biotics. At the first suspicion of any soreness of the nipple it is wise to take the baby off that breast at the next feed and to express the milk instead. If the crack is really bad your doctor may suggest that you continue to express the milk for a while, or wear a nipple shield until it has healed.

Always remember to wash the nipples well before and after feeds, drying them well afterwards, and applying a little lanoline if they are hard. It is equally important to wash the hands before feeding the baby, to prevent the possibility of infecting the nipples.

If a breast abscess should develop, it is nearly always necessary to stop feeding baby, at any rate from the affected breast, but your doctor will advise you.

Overfeeding : This diagnosis has too often been erroneously made in the past, and is still rather a bogey. As long as the feeds are not too frequent, and baby is not forced to take more than he wants at a feed, he can be

PLATE XII.

trusted to know when he has had sufficient. Twenty minutes is usually quite long enough, and many babies get what they want in much less time. If in his eagerness he has taken too much, he will return it with his wind. Loose, green and frequent motions are far more often caused by anxiety and frustration than by overfeeding. These feelings are just as likely to be experienced by a baby as by an adult.

Underfeeding : There are certain signs that a baby is not getting sufficient food, as follows :—

(*a*) He is sometimes very fretful, never sleeping for more than 1 hour or $1\frac{1}{2}$ hours after each feed, and then waking and crying. This stage passes, sometimes rather quickly, and he becomes almost too quiet, appears perfectly good, but is listless and pale.

(*b*) Only small gain in weight, persisting over a period of three weeks, is another indication. Sometimes the weight remains stationary or there is even some loss. Look round for other causes, such as teething or the onset of a cold, both of which may be accompanied by loss of appetite. If there are no other causes, then baby cannot be getting enough to satisfy him.

(*c*) In an underfed baby having breast milk, the motions are often frequent, and consist of greenish mucus. But if he is not getting enough cow's milk, the motions are infrequent and hard.

(*d*) Every baby should have a nice covering of fat, giving him rounded contours. If this is missing, ask yourself why.

(*e*) You may suspect that your supplies of breast

milk are diminishing because you notice that your breasts are not so full as they were, especially towards the end of the day. But do not suppose that because your milk looks " watery," it is not satisfying the baby ; breast milk always does look more watery than cow's, especially at the beginning of a feed, because it contains less fat. Though the quantity may diminish, the quality very rarely deteriorates ; it is almost never found that the mother's milk is harming the baby or failing to nourish him, as long as the quantity is sufficient.

By far the most effective way to increase the supply of milk is to have more rest and relaxation and a contented frame of mind. Privacy when feeding is also helpful ; this is for no prudish reason, but because it ensures a greater degree of relaxation. Try to increase your fluid intake, especially with a milky drink taken about half an hour before the feed. Make quite sure that both breasts are empty after the feed, by expressing by hand what is left. Some women find it helpful to sponge the breasts with hot and cold water alternately, and when they are dry to massage them with olive oil.

Complementary feeding : Sometimes when the mother's supply of milk is rather small, and during the time when she is trying to increase it, complementary feeding may be necessary. This means that baby is fed first of all at both breasts until they are empty, and then is given as much as he will take of a previously prepared feed, from either bottle or spoon, the whole process taking not more than 20 minutes. To work out the approximate amount which you will need to offer baby after the breast feed, estimate his total needs for each feed according to the advice given on page 131. Make up three-quarters of this amount from either diluted cow's milk or a dried milk, according to the directions given in the next chapter, and offer him this. In time you will be able to estimate just how much he will need, but it is always safer to make up too much rather than too little.

You may find that you can satisfy baby completely with breast milk only at some feeds—usually the first two—and will only need to give the extra food at the other feeds. It is most important to remember that baby must be put to the breast at each feed, because his sucking is the best stimulus to the flow of milk. To miss a breast feed in the hope that there will be more milk for the next day does not work out in practice. If breast feeds are regularly missed, the supply will certainly diminish in time.

Food supplements

Vitamins : During the first three months a breast-fed baby should get all the vitamins he needs through his mother's milk, provided she is having her own supplements. But nevertheless, it is a good plan to start him earlier than three months with cod liver oil and orange juice in very small doses and gradually to increase them. You may start with literally one drop of the Ministry of Food preparations in an ounce of boiled water, and give the mixture during one of the wakeful periods between feeds. Or the cod liver oil can be given separately from an egg-spoon, to be sure that he gets it. (See pages 153–154 for more information on this question.)

Iron : Some breast-fed babies may be a little anæmic at first, especially if their mothers have this tendency. It is usually shown by pallor of the lips, and is the type that quickly responds to iron by mouth. Breast milk contains very little of this essential mineral, and if any is needed, your doctor will advise you about a suitable preparation to give after feeds.

Boiled water : This is usually necessary only in hot weather, when the baby is losing fluid by perspiration, or as a vehicle for orange juice.

The nursing mother's health

Diet : The advice about diet for the expectant mother (pages 20–25) applies also during the months of breast-feeding, if good supplies of milk are to be maintained and the mother's health safeguarded. The vitamin supplements are allowed to nursing mothers, too, and are a valuable addition to the diet.

You may find that you tend to be thirsty and need quite an increased amount of fluids.

Whether certain articles in the mother's diet cause digestive upsets in the baby is a controversial subject. Certainly some mothers can eat as much raw fruit, pickles, onions and spices as they please and have thriving, contented babies. But others with babies who tend to have " colic " may suspect a cause in their own diet,

and will want to be on the safe side and cut out such
articles (except for fruit, which is safe in small quantities).
Alcohol and nicotine are excreted in the milk in very
small amounts, so moderation in these is advisable.
Phenobarbitone may also pass into the milk in small
quantity, so where the baby already tends to be too
sleepy, the mother should avoid it. But a baby with an
anxious temperament might well benefit.

Several of the common laxatives may possibly be
excreted in breast milk and affect the baby. If anything
is needed by the mother, the safest is liquid paraffin.
Incidentally, this is the best one to use when hæmorrhoids
are present, as they commonly are during the first few
months after a confinement.

Rest : A nursing mother may find it difficult to obtain
all the sleep she wants for her physical and emotional
needs, especially if the baby is having a night feed and
if she has a toddler, too. But she should make every
effort to secure adequate rest, even if it means neglecting
the house a little, otherwise her breast milk will tend to
diminish in quantity. An hour's complete rest some
time during the day is ideal, if it can be managed. One
suggestion which often works very well is for the mother
to go to bed during the evening and allow her husband
to bring the baby along for his feed at 10 p.m. or so,
and change him and put him down in his cot afterwards.
But whether you can manage these suggestions or not,
always try to think of baby's feed-times as opportunities
for rest and relaxation for yourself. Put your feet up
and make yourself thoroughly comfortable before you

begin. In many cases where the mother finds breast-feeding exhausting, it is because she is tense instead of relaxed during the feeds.

Breast-feeding during a mother's illness : The ordinary infections such as influenza, tonsilitis, or even measles or scarlet fever, do not usually contaminate the mother's milk, and are no reason for taking the baby off the breast, but the final decision about this must rest with your doctor. If he does advise bottle-feeding for a few days, express the milk from your breasts at regular intervals, both to decrease your own discomfort and to ensure the continuance of lactation after you are better again.

It may be that during the few days when the mother is feeling really ill the amount of milk produced will decrease, and therefore it may be necessary to put the baby on to complementary feeds temporarily. (See page 139.) But as the fever abates the normal milk supply will return again and the complementary feeds may be stopped.

Should the mother have had a recent tuberculosis infection, it is wiser for her not to attempt to feed the baby, as the strain might cause the lesion to flare up again.

Breast-feeding and menstruation : Breast-feeding usually delays the re-starting of menstruation after a confinement, but it may appear before breast-feeding is finished. If so, it does not usually affect either the milk or the baby, and there is therefore no reason to take the baby off the breast at this time.

Breast-feeding and pregnancy : Although conception is unlikely during breast-feeding, it is possible. If it is suspected, a definite diagnosis can be obtained by means of special urine tests even quite early in the pregnancy. In most cases it is wise to take the baby off the breast if another pregnancy is confirmed, for the sake of all the three concerned.

Mental attitude : How the mother thinks and feels may affect her breast milk supplies as much as her physical health does. Nervous tension, emotional upsets and worry are all detrimental, and must be avoided as far as possible. Try to cultivate instead a calm, contented outlook. Mothers of first babies are often tempted to worry about tiny deviations from " normal," but try to resist this temptation, because your very worry can harm the baby indirectly. Remember that ordinarily healthy babies are quite tough little creatures, with an amazingly strong hold on life. If you have any doubts or questions, your doctor and the staff at the local Infant Welfare Centre are there to help.

Bottle-feeding

If in spite of your taking all the steps outlined in the previous chapter, you find it is not possible for you to feed baby yourself, consult your doctor or the doctor at the Clinic before you put baby on the bottle. But please do not feel that you are a failure ; set to work instead to make a success of bottle-feeding.

The choice of feed lies between modified cow's milk, dried milk, condensed milk or evaporated milk.

Cow's milk

Human milk and cow's milk differ quite perceptibly, as the following percentage table shows :—

	Water	Casein	Albumin	Protein Total	Sugar	Fat
Human milk	87·58	0·80	1·21	2·01	6·37	3·74
Cow's milk	87·27	2·88	0·51	3·39	4·94	3·68

To sum up : (a) The total protein content is much higher in cow's milk, and the protein is mostly in the form of casein and not in the more digestible form of albumin.

(b) The sugar content is quite markedly lower, and therefore additional sugar must be added to "humanise" the milk.

(c) When the cow's milk is diluted to make its protein content resemble that of human milk, the fat content is much lowered. The cod liver oil, which is given primarily for its vitamin content, is also useful as an additional source of fat.

Nevertheless, with all its differences, cow's milk provides a very good substitute for breast milk and can be used with a quiet mind. It may be obtained as :—

Ordinary milk, which contains an unlimited number of organisms, although all ordinary precautions are taken.

Tuberculin-tested milk : This is milk from a herd of cows which have passed a veterinary examination and the tuberculin test. The cows are re-tested every three months, and the milk itself must pass a dye test for its bacteriological content. This milk may be pasteurised.

Pasteurised milk : Milk which has been kept at a temperature of 145 to 150 degrees Fahrenheit for 30 minutes, i.e., the milk is heated enough to kill germs.

T.T. pasteurised milk is the best variety to use, plain T.T. or pasteurised milk being a good second best.

It is best to *boil* all milk for children under a year old ; the vitamin content is not much altered, and can easily be made up by giving him cod liver oil and orange juice. The chief advantage is that boiling kills all pathogenic organisms, especially the tubercle bacillus, and also makes milk more digestible. If you can get T.T. pasteurised milk, you can begin to give it unboiled after the first year ; if the milk is not pasteurised, you should continue to boil it until the child is 5 years old. After the milk is boiled, it should be poured into a previously scalded jug and covered, and then cooled quickly by standing the jug in a bowl of cold running water.

Warm milk is a wonderful medium for germs to multiply in, so do not give them the chance to get in ! If you live where the milk supply is doubtful, or you cannot keep it fresh, or if you are going to travel, then you should choose a dried milk.

Goat's milk : This is similar in composition to cow's milk, though it contains rather more protein and less sugar. It is quite suitable for babies, provided it is modified in the ways suggested for cow's milk. Its special usefulness is in those cases of infantile eczema which are thought to be due to an allergic reaction to some of the proteins in cow's milk.

Method of using cow's milk

The simplest way of modifying fresh cow's milk is to add boiled water and sugar to it after it has been boiled and cooled. For normal babies during the first three or four months, it is customary to make the mixture of two-thirds milk and one-third water, and to give one small teaspoonful of sugar for each pound of the baby's weight per day. If, however, the stools are loose and frothy, the sugar should be reduced by half for the time being.

As already stated, baby needs daily $2\frac{1}{2}$ oz. milk per lb. of his weight. Suppose that baby weighs 12 lb., then work out the quantities for him : 12 times $2\frac{1}{2}$ oz. is 30 oz. ; if he is having five feeds a day, he will therefore require about 6 oz. of the milk mixture at each feed. So add 2 oz. of boiled water to 4 oz. of boiled milk, and stir in $2\frac{1}{2}$ small teaspoonfuls of sugar (using a spoon which has been boiled). But remember that these quantities are only a guide. If baby takes every drop and is hungry again quite soon, you must make up 1 oz. more at each feed, and let him take what he requires. The proportions of milk to water may be gradually increased, until at about eight months baby has it undiluted, though still boiled, and with only 1 teaspoonful sugar per bottle.

Other ways of modifying cow's milk

(*a*) Add a 2-grain tablet of sodium citrate to each bottle—this makes the curd formed by the action of the juices in the stomach on the protein of the milk more easily digested, as it is finer. This should be used only if baby is not digesting his milk properly.

(*b*) Barley water may be used instead of ordinary water for diluting milk, if the doctor recommends it.

(*c*) The doctor may advise the addition of some special preparation, such as Benger's Food, to the milk, which makes it more digestible for some babies.

(*d*) Cow's milk can also be modified by the addition of extra cereals for those babies who tend to posset a great deal. The suggested proportions are 1 dessert-spoonful Farex or other baby cereal to 4-5 oz. of the milk mixture. The hole in the bottle teat will probably have to be enlarged for this thickened feed. (See " Posseting " in Minor Ailments, page 196.)

Dried milk

The advantages of dried milk over fresh milk are that milk powder is almost sterile, its composition is stable, it can be used under all sorts of conditions (for example, when travelling), and it is usually more digestible, because the protein curds have been modified by the drying process.

National Dried Milk may be taken for children under 2 years as an alternative to fresh cow's milk. Both full-cream and half-cream strength may be obtained, and supplies are at the rate of 1 tin (equivalent to 7 pints of liquid milk) per week to start with. It costs 2s. 4d. a tin ; or may be supplied free in some cases. This National Dried Milk is a good all-round product and can be used quite confidently.

Then there are the half-cream and full-cream dried milks made by many reputable baby-food firms, such as Cow and Gate, Ostermilk, Trufood, S.M.A. (John Wyeth & Brother), etc. The half-cream milk is intended for use during the first six to eight weeks of life and not for longer unless baby is very delicate. Follow medical advice on the matter, however. If you use these proprietary dried milks, you are still entitled to 1 pint of cheap liquid milk a day, so the expense is not much greater.

Most full-cream milks are made so that one level measureful of the milk powder mixed with 1 oz. of water reconstitutes 1 oz. of full-strength cow's milk, which, of course, is not given to baby without dilution. Therefore, when calculating the amounts required, it is often wise to add more water than is stated on the tin.

Suppose baby requires 5 oz. of milk mixture per feed ; make it by mixing 4 level measurefuls of milk powder with 5 oz. of boiled water, and to this add as usual the level teaspoonful of sugar. When he requires 6 oz. per

feed, then you will give 5 measures of the milk and 6 oz.
of boiled water. When changing over from half-cream
to full-cream dried milk, do it gradually. At first, introduce 1 measure of the full-cream into each feed, then
2 and then 3, the measures of half-cream being correspon-
dingly reduced. About three days should be allowed to
make the change complete.

Condensed milk

Condensed milk, sweetened, is sometimes used for
premature babies or in other special cases. A small
teaspoonful of the milk is diluted with 2 tablespoonfuls
of water to make a normal milk solution. The carbo-
hydrate, or sugar, content is high and the fat and protein
low, but if the use of this mixture is combined with
the giving of cod liver oil and perhaps a little fresh
cow's milk, it is fairly satisfactory as long as it is used
only under medical supervision.

Evaporated milk

Reliable preparations of evaporated milk, such as
Carnation and Libby's, are easily digested by babies, and
can be thoroughly recommended for infant feeding.
Instructions are given on the actual tins about the
quantities of evaporated milk, boiled water and sugar
required for babies of different weights, and these offer
good general guidance, to be modified as necessary.

Equipment and method

Perhaps the greatest disadvantage of artificial feeding
compared with breast milk is the increased risk of intro-

ducing infection with all the utensils which must be used. Gastro-enteritis is the most common result of such infection. Great care must therefore be taken to sterilise all feeding equipment and to keep it sterile until required. You should always wash your hands thoroughly and dry them on a clean towel before starting to prepare a feed.

You will need at least two bottles (either upright or boat-shaped), teats, a jug for mixing, a measuring glass, a spoon, a bottle brush and a large bowl in which to keep it all. Before preparing the feed, everything but the brush should have been boiled and afterwards kept under boiled water in the bowl, which is covered with a large plate or a clean cloth. The mixture of dried, fresh or evaporated milk is then prepared in the jug and poured into the bottle, and the teat is put on.

If you can rinse the bottle and teat right away after the feed, you will find it easier to remove the remaining traces of milk. If you wish, you can use one of the liquid detergents and rinse well, then sterilise later on.

A satisfactory alternative to the boiling method of sterilising the equipment is to use the Milton routine, as detailed in the makers' instructions.

Make up the mixture as near to the time of the feed as you conveniently can. Warm milk is a wonderful breeding ground for germs, and however careful you may have been, you may have introduced the odd one : this odd one will not matter if the feed is given fairly quickly, but if it is kept for hours at a nice, warm temperature, the one germ may have multiplied.

Baby likes his feed not too hot and not too cold, but just at about the temperature which seems warm to the back of your hand when you shake a few drops from the bottle on to it. The temperature of the bottle can be modified until it is just right by standing it in a large jug of hot or cold water, as required. If baby is a slow feeder, you can wrap the bottle in a cloth to keep it warm.

Do not give the baby his bottle when he is lying down in his cot or pram, but hold him comfortably in a sitting position ; this will enable him to get his wind up more easily. (See Plate XI.) As with a breast-fed baby, it is advisable to stop about half-way through the feed, to allow some wind to come up. (See pages 129–130.)

Be sure to see that baby can get his food quickly enough ; very often the hole in the teat is too small, and he has to suck very hard to get his milk. Remember that when a baby feeds at the breast the milk comes very easily ; in fact it is often projected into the baby's mouth. If the hole is too small, sterilise a needle by pressing the eye end into a cork, and holding the point in a flame. Then put the red-hot point into the teat to enlarge the hole, or make a second hole if necessary. To test the size of the hole, hold the bottle teat downwards and count the drops as they fall—60 drops to the minute give a nice easy flow when the baby is sucking. Always see that the bottle is tilted sufficiently to keep the teat full of milk, otherwise baby will swallow air and add to his " wind." And the teat should not be allowed to become flattened by the creation of a partial vacuum inside the bottle. If you have a boat-shaped bottle, take the valve off to allow air to enter as the milk is sucked out. If it is an upright one, gently draw the teat out of baby's mouth from time to time, to let air get in.

Food supplements

Cod liver oil, in one form or another, is essential to baby's health. It gives him the vitamins A and D, so vital in the prevention of rickets, the growth of bones, and in providing resistance to infection. It is customary to start with one or two drops a day and work up gradually to the full dose at five or six months, which is 2 teaspoonfuls of ordinary cod liver oil, or 1 teaspoonful of the Ministry of Food cod liver oil. There are also good concentrated preparations on the market, such as Adexolin (10 drops), Radiostoleum (10 drops) and halibut liver oil (3 drops). Since, however, there is the danger that a few infants are susceptible to large doses of vitamin D, it is recommended by the Ministry of Health that babies having dried milks containing these vitamins (which include National Dried Milk) should be given only 7-8 drops of cod liver oil daily. As soon as the change is made to fresh cow's milk, however, the full dose is required, until the age of five. Breast-fed babies also need the full dose.

It is not wise to add the oil to the feeds, because so much of it may stick to the inside of the bottle. Most babies take it quite well from an egg-spoon, and many of them really enjoy it. Do not pull a face as you give it, or otherwise inadvertently prejudice baby against it.

If he does make a fuss and is apt to spit it out, try giving it when he is in the bath. But if he really objects to it, give the most concentrated preparation with his orange juice.

Continue giving these vitamins during the summer.

Vitamin C, another important factor in building up resistance to infection, is found in many fruits and vegetables. There are several sources suitable for babies. The full dose of fresh orange juice at 6 months of age is 4 teaspoonfuls ; of the Ministry of Food orange juice, 2 ; rosehip syrup, 3 ; and blackcurrant juice, 9 teaspoonfuls. Start with 1-2 drops only, diluted with 1 oz. water and a little sugar if necessary. If any difficulty is experienced in giving or obtaining these, vitamin C (ascorbic acid) tablets may be added to the feeds ; they are sold in 5 mg. and 25 mg. strength ; 5 mg. is sufficient for a tiny baby, and 25 mg. for the 6 months old child.

Vitamin C drinks can be given as a thirst-quencher, preferably during a wakeful period between feeds.

Iron : As in the case of breast-fed babies, iron may be needed by mouth if any anæmia is present. But many well-known dried milk firms make special brands containing iron, and one of these may be given. However, be guided by your doctor about this.

S.M.A. dried milk (John Wyeth & Brother) contains all these supplements, including vitamin C. It keeps indefinitely, mixes almost instantaneously with water, and is therefore excellent for travelling or for use where vitamin supplements are difficult to obtain.

Mixed Feeding and Weaning

When a baby has completed his fourth month (or weighs 15 lb.), milk may not be sufficient to meet all his needs, so it is a good plan to begin offering new foods from this stage onwards. But they must be thought of as additions, and should not replace breast or cow's milk for several months yet. Indeed, if supplies are good, it is better for the child's physical and emotional well-being if at least some breast-feeding can be continued until the ninth or tenth month.

The first additions are specially prepared baby cereal, of which there are several good ones on the market, bone broth and purée of vegetables and fruit, and hard rusks or crusts. Along with the previously mentioned vitamins, these additions will supply all the additional nutritional requirements, will give practice in biting and chewing, will accustom him to new tastes and textures, and get him used to using a cup and spoon.

But during this stage it is important to remember that there is no hurry. The mother's attitude should be one of loving guidance and encouragement. The operation should never become a battle, with the mother forcing her will on the baby. Any baby with an ounce of character will have a lovely time spitting out all the spoonfuls he is made to take in his reaction against forcing ! Of course, he will win every time, and the mother tends to feel discomfited and incompetent, and the baby will begin to associate food with unpleasantness and to use food refusal as a means of asserting his independence.

Always remember that it is no reflection on either mother or child if he should be a little slower in accepting new foods than the baby next door.

Here in outline are the stages through which you should try to lead him :

At Four Months or when 15 lbs. in Weight (or earlier if advised by your doctor)

Make a paste of 1 teaspoonful of pre-cooked cereal, with 1 oz. of reconstituted dried milk or diluted cow's milk (3 parts of milk : 1 part of water) and a pinch of sugar. Cow's milk must be boiled, and the mixture just warm. Give this from a small teaspoon just before the 10 a.m. feed. Be patient if he does not like it to begin with. Sometimes it is more acceptable after a breast or bottle feed, when he is in a more contented frame of mind, but when he is used to it, offer it again before the feed. (These quantities can be gradually increased until at seven or eight months he is having about 4 teaspoonfuls in 2–3 oz. of boiled milk.)

Immediately before the 2 p.m. feed, offer 1–2 teaspoonfuls of bone broth or red " juice " from the joint. The broth can be home-made, but there are excellent tinned preparations now on the market. Some babies object to savoury flavours at first. If so, help them to get used to these gradually by giving instead a little cereal and milk, to which a little bone broth has been added. Increase the proportion of broth slowly, until that

alone is given with the cereal, and then the broth
alone.

A fortnight later, when the above extras have been
accepted readily, the same amount of cereal may be given
before the 6 p.m. feed, and the amount of broth increased
at 2 p.m.

From now on, the midday meal may be progressively
supplemented, until at six or seven months it includes
sieved vegetables, half of a lightly cooked yolk of egg,
or $\frac{1}{2}$ tablespoonful of mashed steamed plaice, or 1 teaspoonful of grated raw cheese.

At About Seven Months

If the baby is happily accustomed to small amounts of
the additions so far suggested, now is the time to start
omitting breast or bottle feeds.

The 2 p.m. feed is probably the most convenient to
drop first, because the baby is already having a substantial first course which can be followed by a little
stewed apple and custard or well-cooked milk pudding.
If necessary 1–2 oz. of cow's milk (still boiled) can be
given to finish the meal : it should be offered from a
cup or beaker. Dried milk may be more reliable in hot
weather or in certain other circumstances, but on the
whole it is better to let the baby become accustomed to
fresh milk. Until he is fully seven months, it should
be diluted in the proportions of 7 of milk : 1 of water,
and it must still be boiled.

The next bottle or breast feed to be omitted is the
10 a.m. one. At this meal the cereal may be increased,

and a little scrambled or boiled egg or crumbled crisply fried bacon added.   Milk is given from a cup or beaker.

A week later try dropping the 6 p.m. bottle or breast feed.   But if the baby still seems to need the solace which sucking gives before he settles down to sleep, by all means continue it for a few weeks longer.

At Eight or Nine Months

During this stage meals can be gradually brought to coincide with those of the family.   The early morning feed may be dropped, and a Vitamin C drink and rusk given instead.   The old 10 a.m. feed may be brought forward to the family breakfast time, and the midday meal becomes dinner.   A tea-meal is now introduced, consisting of a hard rusk with honey and butter, sand-wiches of yeast extract or egg or cream cheese, and a little milk pudding.   At bed-time a drink of milk is usually sufficient at this age.

The 10 p.m. feed : If the baby is gaining well and is hard to awaken at 10 p.m., the experiment of dropping this feed may be tried at any time after five months. If he wakes in the night hungry, you will know that he is not yet ready for the omission, and you should try again in a few weeks' time.   Some babies need this last feed up to eight or nine months, and it all depends upon the indivi-dual baby.   This is often the last breast feed to be dropped.

Few mothers experience much discomfort in their breasts if the weaning period is a very gradual one, as indicated above.   Sucking is the chief stimulus to the milk supplies and, as it gradually diminishes, so does the milk. But it helps to drink rather less, and in cases of real discomfort you should consult your doctor, who will be able to help by prescribing pills.

Feeds During Travelling

If an artificially fed young baby must be fed on a journey, try to have all the necessary utensils as sterile as possible. Boil up the bottle, teat and mixing spoon and jug (if any) as usual, and wrap them in freshly laundered cloths just before the journey. Boil the milk, cool it, then pour into a vacuum flask (previously scalded, and cooled with cold boiled water). Boiling water to dilute and warm the milk, or to mix with dried milk, can also be carried in a flask. Remember that the best temperature for the multiplication of germs is at blood heat, so do not be tempted to keep a feed at this temperature for several hours. For children who need a cereal food, the milk can be put into a vacuum flask at boiling-point, then poured into a cup and a ready-cooked cereal added to it when required. Strained vegetables or fruit may be carried in a flask or in the tin.

General Hints on Weaning

(a) This chart is intended to be a guide, not a blue-print, for each baby has individual requirements and tastes according to size and constitution. The Family Doctor will be pleased to advise if necessary.

(b) Encourage a calm, happy atmosphere at meal-times, and avoid anxiety and fuss. Let baby take his time over weaning.

(c) Cod liver oil, or a concentrated preparation of Vitamin A and D, is still important. For obvious reasons, a suitable time to give it is while baby is in the bath, as already suggested.

(d) Offer the new food from a teaspoon, starting with one only at first. But the thickened feeds can be given from a bottle with a large-holed teat if new methods are unacceptable at first, and if the doctor has expressly ordered the addition of cereal.

(e) A good broth can be made like this :—Break up 1 lb. veal or beef bones, cover with water, add 1 teaspoonful of vinegar, and simmer for 4–7 hours. Add all kinds of vegetables, and simmer for another hour, add a little Marmite—strain ; when cool, remove the fat. This broth should keep for 2 or 3 days in a very cool place. There are also good tinned varieties for babies on the market, e.g., Heinz, Nestlés, Trufood, Robinson's Robsoup.

(f) Rusks may be made at home by baking fingers of bread in a slow oven until hard, or you can buy rusks such as Ovaltine or Farley's. You can let the baby practice chewing on them even before the teeth appear.

(g) Breast-feeding is of great emotional value, and should be continued as long as reasonably possible.

Weaning chart

Four–five months

6 a.m.   Breast or bottle feed.

10 a.m.   Cow's milk, 6 teaspoons ; water, 2

teaspoons ;　sugar,　½　teaspoon — or
1 oz. reconstituted dried milk, thickened
with 1 teaspoon Farex, Robrex, Cerex,
Trufood Cereal, Scott's Twin Pack, or
Robinson's Pre-cooked Groats.

Follow by a breast or bottle feed (5–6 oz.).

2 p.m.　2–4 teaspoons broth or red gravy.
Breast or bottle feed.

4.30 p.m.　Vitamin C drink (orange juice, rosehip
syrup, etc.).　Rusk.

6 p.m.　Same as at 10 a.m.

10 p.m.　Breast or bottle feed.

Five and a half months

6 a.m.　Breast or bottle feed.

10 a.m.　Increase cereal mixture :　1½ oz. milk ;
1½ teaspoons cereal.
Breast or bottle feed.

2 p.m.　Thicken broth with a little mashed potato
or cereal.　Add 1 teaspoon sieved or
homogenised vegetables.
Breast or bottle feed.

4.30 p.m.　Vitamin C drink (orange juice, rosehip
syrup, etc.).　Rusk.

6 p.m.　Same as at 10 a.m.

10 p.m.　Breast or bottle feed if required.

Six months

6 a.m.　Breast or bottle feed.

10 a.m.　Rusk.　Increase quantity of cereal mixture

B.B.—11

where necessary. If cow's milk is used, gradually increase strength.

Breast or bottle feed.

2 p.m.   Same as at $5\frac{1}{2}$ months, with addition of half a lightly boiled egg yolk or 1 teaspoonful grated cheese or $\frac{1}{2}$ tablespoonful pounded steamed fish.

Breast or bottle feed.

4.30 p.m.   Vitamin C drink (orange juice, rosehip syrup, etc.). Rusk.

6 p.m.   Same as at 10 a.m.

10 p.m.   Breast or bottle feed if required.

Seven months

6 a.m.   Breast or bottle feed.

10 a.m.   Cow's milk, now undiluted, with cereal.

Small breast feed (or may be omitted).

2 p.m.   First course as at 6 months, followed by stewed apple and custard, or well cooked milk pudding.

No bottle or breast feed.

4–4.30 p.m.   Vitamin C drink (orange juice, rosehip syrup, etc.). Rusk.

6 p.m.   As at 10 a.m. Bottle or breast feed useful to settle baby to sleep.

10 p.m.   Bottle or breast feed if required.

Eight–twelve months (meals to fit in with family)

On waking :   Vitamin C drink. Rusk.

Breakfast :   Fried bread and tomato ; or crisp

	crumbled bacon ; *or* boiled or scrambled egg ; and/or cereals as before. Toast and honey, if necessary. Milk to drink.
Elevenses :	Drink of milk or fruit juice or water.
Dinner : 12–12.30 p.m.	Minced chicken, liver or lamb may be added, and ordinary vegetables introduced in to the first course.
	Second course as before.
Tea :	Hard crust with butter and honey, *or* hard apple *or* carrot. Helping of pudding or fruit. Sandwiches of Marmite, tomato or grated cheese, or egg.
6 p.m.	Breast feed, if necessary, *or* a milky drink, with or without cereal.

From one to two years

The baby has now reached the stage when he may have his meals with the family, sitting in his high-chair at the table with the rest. For the first few months of the period he will probably need some help with his meals, and it may be more convenient for him to start his dinner a little earlier than the others. On the whole, however, the best plan is to pay as little attention to him as possible.

His tools are a spoon, with possibly a pusher as well at the end of this stage. Even if you need to help him, he should have a spoon of his own and should be encouraged to use it as much as possible. He will also need his own cup or beaker (use one which is not readily tipped over), and a plate with a raised edge to lessen spilling.

His table manners will be very simple at this stage. He will learn unconsciously from sharing in the family meals, but there should never be any nagging insistence on cleanliness. It is natural for him to experiment with his food, and he can't be expected to be very tidy in eating while he is still so young. His good appetite and his happy relationship with you are of far more importance than absence of mess during meal-times. Provide him with a good bib, preferably one which covers his sleeves as well as his front. Spread a piece of Americancloth or plastic material under his high-chair to save the carpet. It only takes seconds to remove the traces of dinner spread over his face and the cloth. He may be going through an independent, self-assertive stage at this time, and it is best to use this in a constructive way by letting him manage his own meals, however messily, rather than to frustrate him by helping him to eat tidily.

His food, though still needing some modification, can be much the same as the family has. Different foods, e.g. cauliflower and potato, should be placed separately on the plate, and not mashed up together ; in this way the small child will learn to appreciate the different flavours of foods. Give small helpings of each course ; he can always have more if he is ready for them. Cooked vegetables need no longer be sieved, and breakfast cereals may be of the adult type.

Milk, if not pasteurised, must be boiled. The quantity

to aim at should be approximately 1 pint each day, served in various ways, such as with cereals, in milk puddings and soups, and as a drink. Some children find milk too fatty, and, if so, give it skimmed and flavoured with a little yeast extract. Skimmed milk is still rich in protein and calcium, and is not to be despised.

Cod liver oil, or a preparation equivalent in vitamin value, should be continued in the same amounts as before.

Chewing should be encouraged to benefit the teeth and gums. Hard rusks and pieces of raw apple or carrot can be given for this purpose, especially after a meal, when they also have a cleaning effect.

Diet chart for one to two years

Before breakfast :	Vitamin C drink, e.g., orange or tomato juice or rosehip syrup. Rusk.
Breakfast : about 8 a.m.	A small piece of crisp bacon and fried egg or tomato ; *or* lightly boiled or scrambled egg with bread and butter ; *or* omelette flavoured with chopped ham or parsley ; *or* sieved tomato or Marmite sandwich ; *or* grilled herrings or smoked haddock.
	followed by : Cereal, e.g., porridge, Weetabix, Farex, cornflakes, puffed wheat ; with milk and sugar or stewed or fresh fruit and sugar.
	followed by : Toast and marmalade, jelly or honey if required. Milk to drink.

Mid-morning :   Drink of orange juice *or* water.

Dinner :   Potatoes and vegetables with good broth or gravy *and* one of the following : Tender meat, fish, rabbit, liver, chicken (well minced or pounded until baby has sufficient teeth to enable him to chew), brains, sweetbread, tripe, eggs or grated cheese. Raw salads may be introduced in small quantities.

followed by : Any simple milk pudding ; *or* light sponge pudding ; *or* jellies made with milk and egg ; *or* baked apple ; *or* stewed fruit (with pips and skins removed) ; *or* ripe banana. Give custard or junket with fruit.

3 p.m.   Drink of water *or* lemonade *or* orangeade made with fresh fruit.

Tea :   Sandwiches made from wholemeal bread
4.30 p.m.   and any of the following fillings : tomato, grated carrot, grated cheese, Marmite, cress, lettuce, apple, honey, treacle, jam, chocolate spread ; *or* a salad made with tomato, carrot, etc. Plain cake. Milk to drink, flavoured if necessary with dash of cocoa or tea. It is a good plan to get baby to eat a good tea, and then supper can be omitted.

Supper (if   Give a drink of Bengers, Horlicks,
necessary) :   Ovaltine or Bourn-vita and milk. Piece of hard eating apple.

The Growing Baby

Growth does not commence abruptly at birth—physical growth has been progressing throughout the pre-natal period, and there is also some mental development during this time. The child can move and feel, and may even hear, and it is certainly sensitive to vibrations in the fluid in which it lies.

The process of birth is one of the greatest changes that occur during the whole life of the individual. The baby is forcibly expelled from his warm, snug home, and immediately begins the struggle for life. He must now breathe and suck, and so, from being entirely dependent upon his mother for all his requirements, he begins to fend for himself. No wonder that so often his first reaction is to utter a cry of protest. Although the new-born baby knows from the beginning how to breathe, cry and suck, his other movements are at first few and aimless.

In comparison with the young of other members of the animal world a child develops and grows slowly ; even so, during the first two years of life prodigious changes take place : he not only gains in weight and height, but he gains control of his movements, he learns to relate things seen and heard to himself, and in fact, he has gone a long way along the road which leads to a really independent existence. Thus, during the early years the growth of the body and the growth of the mind go hand-in-hand.

The baby is not born as an " adult in miniature "—
indeed, many of the special tissues have to develop and
grow during the first few years of life. At birth the
nervous system is in quite an immature state, but during
these early years the brain develops almost to its adult
size, as do the bones of the skull which cover it. At the
same time there is much growth in the bones of the arms
and legs and also in the muscle tissues. We can judge
the rate of growth by keeping a check on the child's
weight and height. This does not mean that a baby
should be weighed very often—once a week is quite
sufficient for a normal baby, and after a few months a
fortnightly weighing is adequate. Keep a note of the
weights, for it is interesting to refer to this record.

Your baby will be weighed at the Infant Welfare
Centre, should you be able to take him there, and you
will be given a record card. If there is no Centre within
reach, then you can hire scales or have the baby weighed
at the chemist's shop. This will mean that on returning
home you must weigh his clothes on the kitchen scales
and subtract this weight from the figure already noted ;
thus you get the weight of your baby naked, which is
more satisfactory if useful comparisons are to be made.

Weight and height

Weight : During the first week of his life a baby nearly
always loses weight ; this is because he is adjusting himself to a new way of living, and also because the breast
milk is not in plentiful supply until the fourth day. Then

he gradually begins to gain, until at the end of the first two weeks he is at least back to his birth weight.

After that, and for the first six months of his life, he will often gain at least 6 oz. each week, while between six and twelve months the weekly gain will probably fall to 3 or 4 oz. During the second year the gain is at the rate of roughly $\frac{1}{2}$ lb. per month.

At this rate you will find that at six months of age baby will be more than double his birth weight, and at a year he will be at least three times his birth weight. Do not worry if he gains unevenly, for this is quite usual : one week he may gain only 2 oz., but the following week his gain may be 8 or 10 oz. Should baby fail to make a considerable gain in weight over a period of three weeks, however, medical advice should be sought.

Height : At birth a baby is about 20 inches long, and by the time he is a year old, he will be 28 or 29 inches long. From this time onwards he will grow about $2\frac{1}{2}$ inches each year—but here again the growth is not always steady, especially with the older child, and much depends on the sort of build which the baby has inherited from his parents.

Healthy growth

Many mothers tend to worry if their baby does not weigh as much as the baby next door, but it must be stressed that size in itself is no criterion of health and strength and happiness. Because other babies are bigger than yours, they are not necessarily healthier or better in any way. However, to ensure that your baby can develop the best possible physique within the framework of his inherited tendencies, his daily programme must be carefully thought out to include the following :

A well-balanced diet : Three chapters in this book are devoted to details of infant feeding (see pages 125–166).

An adequate amount of exercise : The really tiny baby gets most of the exercise he requires during the exertions of feeding, bathing and crying. Even at an early age you can turn him on his tummy before bath-time and let him practise lifting up his head : this strengthens the back muscles. By the time baby is two months old he should be ready to have a definite kicking time. This is usually best arranged just before a feed is due, if he is not too hungry, and he will often enjoy a kick then. Loosen his nappies, turn him on his back and let him be free to move as he wishes. As he gets older, he will like to kick against an object such as a board at the end of his cot, or the arm at the end of the settee. In this way he will push himself, and so strengthen his muscles.

The older baby gets much exercise in pulling himself up into the sitting or standing positions. Later on he will roll or shuffle or crawl along in the way which suits him best—and which often causes his parents much amusement. Many mothers fear that such activity will harm him because his muscles are not yet strong enough, and so try to restrain him ; but you can take it as a safe rule that the baby will only attempt to do what he is ready for, and all muscular activity which he himself indulges in will help him to develop properly. When he is tired he will stop. What you should guard against is encouraging him to perform his tricks when he is disinclined, and he should never be made to walk when he is too tired to do so willingly.

The playpen, firmly fixed to the ground, will give him much support at this time. It is always a good plan to introduce a playpen well before he can move around, so that he can get used to playing in it happily ; otherwise, if he is put into it only after he can crawl, he is apt to regard it merely as a restricting cage. Open-air play is also a great advantage—the child of eighteen months to two years will take an interest in a sand-pit and in running up and down little hillocks, and may even manage a small pedal toy.

An adequate amount of rest (see pages 99–101) : It is quite easy for a baby who can walk to over-exert himself. Be sure, therefore, to see that baby gets his full allowance of sleep and that he spends part of his waking time in his chair or pram.

Plenty of fresh air : The healthy baby should be out for at least some part of the day in all weathers except fog. If there is a cold wind, the pram may be placed in a sheltered spot. And when he is indoors there should be some ventilation in the room, by means of an open window, a door or a chimney.

Remember that the skin also needs fresh air, and over-clothing should be avoided. If the young child is allowed to get too hot because of too many clothes, or too heavy cot or pram covers, he will perspire, and this perspiration will clog the pores and make his under-clothes damp, with increased risk of chilling later. The mental and physical processes are also retarded if he is too hot, and he may be thoroughly uncomfortable and irritable. So be on the alert to prevent over-heating as much as you are to prevent chilling. Dress the baby according to the actual temperature of the day, not according to the season.

Emotional security : A calm and friendly atmosphere is as important to the baby's healthy development as good physical care. If he feels himself loved and approved, and is handled with gentle firmness, he will be content and will thrive.

First playthings

A baby's first playthings are very simple. Towards the end of his first year his chief delight will be in anything with which he can make a noise—a tray and a wooden spoon, or a rattle, for instance. Boxes, sauce-pans, round biscuit tins, are all excellent playthings for the one- to two-year-old ; to put the lid on and take it off, to fill and empty, is delight enough. At this age he will want a few wooden bricks of different sizes to pile up and to put in his boxes. He will get great fun from a few floating toys in his bath, and on warm days in the garden he can have a large bowl of water with a few funnels and a mug to pour from. A tray of sand and a wooden spoon to dig in it will keep him happy for a long while.

You must make very sure that all playthings which the baby has are safe. He should not be given beads or buttons which he might swallow. Soft toys should be washable and hygienic ; eyes should be securely fastened. Colours should be fast, for the toy will inevitably be sucked.

There are well-made toys of good design for small children in the Kiddicraft range of Sensible Toys. A wide range of toys for the nursery age is obtainable from Paul and Marjorie Abbatt, 94 Wimpole Street, W.1, and from the baby or toy departments of many of the big stores.

Development of the senses

Touch : To begin with the baby's hands move aimlessly round, but he soon finds that he can feel with them, and often during the feeding process he will handle the breast or the bottle. The ability to grasp out for an object comes later, and rarely occurs until the child is six months old, though before this he will be making experiments by touching and handling his clothing and the sides of his pram or cradle.

Smell : The small baby has a fairly keen sense of smell. He quickly comes to recognise the smell of his mother and of her milk, and will turn towards the breast when he is held near it. This is often demonstrated by the fact that a mother finds it difficult to soothe her child when he is hungry, because he is always wanting to nuzzle into her and be fed.

Hearing : A baby's sense of hearing is usually quite acute. He will jump at a big noise, and soon comes to recognise his mother's and father's voice. Quite young children like the sound of music or singing. By the time he is four months old a baby will turn his head and eyes in the direction of a sound.

If you should have any reason to suspect that the baby's hearing is not normal, seek medical advice without delay. A great deal can be done to help deaf children even at a very early age, and the sooner special training is begun, the less the child will be handicapped in later life.

Sight : The small baby does not like a bright light, and will invariably blink and shut his eyes as a protection against it ; therefore, when he is out of doors, he should be put in the shady part of the garden, or be protected from glare by a suitable canopy. At first his vision is poorly developed, and not until he is at least six to eight weeks old will he show any signs of recognising his mother or of smiling. At five to six months he may be able to appreciate brightly coloured objects, and a little later he will commence to grasp at these objects with his hands. Not until he is about two years old will the child have anything like an adult range of vision.

All little babies squint at times ; this is because they have not learned to focus in any measure, and so they do not control the movements of their eyes. A transitory squint of this type need not give rise to any worry.

Milestones in development

Do not worry if your baby does not follow the exact times and stages given in these paragraphs—remember he is an individual, and he will do all these things when his development has reached the right stage. Your baby is not necessarily backward just because he does not sit up as early as your neighbour's baby did.

Some parents are constantly looking forward to the next stage of their baby's development, and pushing him into it, as if being " forward for his age " were everything to be desired. In this way they tend to miss enjoying the baby as he is. In every stage there are charms and attractions.

Teeth : Some babies are born with teeth already erupted, others may be well over a year old before the first ones appear. Both these extremes are in the " normal " range, but the majority of babies cut their front teeth in the lower gum at about seven months. The others appear at fairly regular intervals, and the full complement of twenty milk teeth is usually present by 2 or 2½ years. The teeth are already formed and present in the gums at birth, and their structure is intimately concerned with the mother's health during pregnancy. In particular, she needs plenty of calcium, and vitamin D to ensure its absorption, hence the importance of milk, cheese, eggs and fish in her diet, and the vitamin supplements (see page 21). For the care of the baby's teeth, see page 116.

The Fontanelles : This is the correct term for the spaces in between the skull bones. When baby is born there are several spaces, the largest being towards the front of the dome of the head. Although there is no bone in these areas to protect the brain, gentle horizontal friction in washing and hair-brushing will do no harm.

At birth the largest fontanelle is roughly diamond-shaped and measures about 2 inches each way. As baby grows the bones of the skull come closer together and the soft area becomes smaller, until it is obliterated altogether. This usually happens before the eighteenth month.

Sitting up : Babies usually try to sit up at about five to six months, that is, they hold on to an object and attempt to pull themselves up ; but they cannot sit up unaided until they are between seven and eight months old, and some babies may be later than this. Mothers often wonder whether they should prop baby up in a sitting position. This is quite permissible after the age of six months, for short periods of 20–30 minutes, or less if the baby is tired ; baby enjoys seeing what is going on around him.

Crawling and standing : At any time between nine and twelve months baby will begin to crawl or shuffle. As soon as he displays any desire to become mobile he should be allowed to try, even if he has not reached the usual age. The same rule applies to standing, because a baby will not try to stand until he is ready to do so— often at ten or eleven months.

Walking : Considering the complexity of the movements involved, babies walk surprisingly early in their lives, usually at about the age of twelve to fifteen months. At first baby will walk holding on to objects, but later he will gain confidence and launch out without any support. You will notice that he tends to walk on his toes, and that later he learns to use the soles of his feet. At the beginning he tends to walk with his feet separated, and perhaps with his toes turned in, to help his balance, but later he modifies this.

Feeding : The mouth and lips are very sensitive parts and the baby soon discovers this, so at the age of six weeks or even earlier he may put his fingers or thumb into his mouth. This habit can be turned to good use, because it is usually fairly easy to teach baby to feed himself, as soon as he starts on more solid food. Many children feed themselves at ten to twelve months, others may find it more difficult to negotiate a spoon, because they will turn it upside down on its way to the mouth, and then find to their great surprise that all the food drops out !

Speaking : The young child begins to make experimental sounds, other than crying, when he is about three months old. He also begins to realise the social value of his vocal efforts, and finds that by crying he can attract attention, and that his mother laughs when he coos and gurgles to her. At seven to eight months he will probably bring out his first word, which is often " Dad-dad," and he then adds words fairly quickly.

Summary : By the time he is a year old baby will probably be crawling and possibly standing and attempting to walk. He will be able to hold a cup and spoon and will make a good effort to feed himself. At this age he will probably have a vocabulary of three or four words, and will wave " Bye-bye " and possibly be able to say it. He will also be quite interested in his toys,

B.B.—12

playing with bricks and rings, and he will enjoy a game of " Peep-bo."

At eighteen months he will probably be able to build with his bricks, he will have quite a number of words in his vocabulary and will be walking well ; at two years he should be running and attempting to climb ; he will probably have control of his bladder by day, and many babies can talk fairly fluently.

The first child usually develops more slowly than the younger members of the family, because he lacks the stimulus of watching and imitating the other older children, but never try to make your child cross his bridges before he is ready.

Characteristics of behaviour

Shyness : Most young babies have a ready smile for anyone who smiles at them, but towards the end of the first year it is usual for them to turn away from strangers. This new shyness does not mean that the baby, who was at first so friendly, is now becoming an unsociable character—it is a sign of growth, and should be treated as such. The baby is now old enough to notice the difference between familiar people and strangers, so it is only right that a stranger should have to win the baby's confidence by his unobtrusive friendliness—and he should never demand it.

Dependence : Many little children in the course of their second year will go through what is commonly known as a " Mummy phase," when they can hardly bear to have mother out of sight or to have a closed door between them. The child is gradually realising that his mother is someone separate from himself and that it is in her power to go away from him. His greatest fear is to be alone and helpless, so he tries his utmost to keep her near him. If the mother makes allowances for his natural feelings and tries to keep at least within sound, and as much within sight as possible, the phase will pass as the child's confidence grows.

Anger : However much a baby is loved, his wishes and those of the grown-ups around him are bound to come into conflict, especially as he becomes more mobile and more experimental. He will regard even reasonable control as despotism, and will often express his anger vividly and forcibly. It is for the adults who have control of the situation to help the child by understanding his point of view, even if it can't always be allowed expression. Give him freedom wherever it is possible, and where it is not, offer him steady love to absorb his anger.

Jealousy : Since very little children are naturally greedy for love, they will feel an intense sense of rivalry with anyone who seems to stand in their way. While a boy admires his father for his strength and skill, he may still feel that he would like to have his mother all for himself. Other children, who are not yet valued as playmates, are looked on at first as intruders and rivals. If a child's tempestuous feelings are met with steadiness and affection, however, they will moderate and will gradually give way to co-operation

Perhaps the greatest potential source of jealousy is a new baby in the home, and this situation may cause different behaviour problems. A mother may deny the existence of jealousy because the toddler shows such apparent affection for the baby in the cot ; so he may, but at the same time, he may be fiercely jealous of the place the baby has taken in his mother's arms and in her attentions. Due allowances must be made for this feeling, which will gradually be dispelled as the toddler regains a sense of security in his mother's affections.

Thumb-sucking : When you consider how important the activity of sucking is to the baby, it is not surprising that he turns to his finger or thumb for comfort. In a young child the habit can be looked on as normal and there is no need to try to prevent it. When the baby is asleep, gently remove the thumb from his mouth. It is not likely that he will become a mouth-breather or spoil the shape of his jaw through sucking his thumb. As he grows older and finds more sources of satisfaction in the world around him, he will most probably give up the habit of his own accord.

Cot-rocking and head-banging : There are a few children who, for some reason which is rather obscure, develop the habit of rocking, either as they sit during the day or while awake during the night, and some will bang their heads on their cots. The performance may be sustained for quite a long time and the parents understandably feel very concerned—the noise is disturbing, and they fear that the child will suffer through losing his rest and may hurt himself. This symptom is commonest in the second year and usually disappears spontaneously, but it may persist for some considerable time. Fortunately, there is no cause for alarm—indeed, this seems to be one of the ways in which a child eases some internal tension and restores his inner equilibrium. It may be possible to anchor the cot if the child moves it violently and to pad the wooden rails ; otherwise it is best to take as little notice as possible. Try to ensure that such a child leads a placid life during his waking hours and is not confined for long periods to his pram.

These problems, so common in the second year, are mentioned here because they often distress parents, who look on them as signs that the child's character is developing along undesirable lines, or that they themselves have failed in some way in the child's management, whereas in fact these are normal phases, which certainly call for patience and understanding, but which need cause no alarm.

As you learn to understand all this more fully, any difficulties which occur will fall into their right perspective. If your child's behaviour in front of visitors, for instance, falls below expectation, you won't be bound to feel that he has let you down, but will wonder first why he needed to behave like that. Even if by misfortune he should be handicapped in some way, your foremost thought will be to help him to compensate for his trouble. If you love your child for what he is, as a person in his own right, you will be giving him the best possible atmosphere in which to develop as he should.

Minor Ailments and their Remedies

If you suspect anything seriously wrong with your baby, you should at once call in your doctor or take baby to the Clinic. But there are some minor conditions which can be treated at home, and mothers may be saved a great deal of worry if they can recognise the signs and deal with them promptly. In this chapter we give a list of nursery troubles and their treatment, covering those most commonly encountered in babies under two years of age.

Prevention of illness

There is still no means of preventing the mild infectious diseases such as mumps, measles, chicken-pox and colds. But it is now possible to guard against the serious conditions of smallpox, whooping cough, tetanus, tuberculosis and poliomyelitis by means of vaccination and immunisation.

Vaccination against smallpox : Smallpox is a very serious illness, with a high death-rate. It is not usually present in England, but is liable to be brought in from abroad from time to time, and to cause sudden epidemics. Vaccination is a good safeguard, and parents are advised to protect their children in this way. The best age is three or four months, because then the risk of complications is almost negligible, while it increases considerably with age.

In these days the ordinary reaction is very slight indeed. At worst the disturbance is a restless 24 hours. About a week after the vaccination a small blister appears at the site ; soon it begins to discharge, and later a black scab forms, falling off to leave a scar. During the acute stage a dry dressing is all that is needed. Only one mark is made, and the child can be taught to think of it as a badge of protection rather than a blemish. The arm is the most convenient site, from the point of view of looking after it during the active stage and of showing the scar to doctors, etc., in later life.

If a baby has a tendency to eczema, the doctor will probably prefer not to vaccinate unless you are going abroad to live in a country where smallpox is prevalent. The presence of eczema carries with it a risk of generalised reaction after vaccination. But this risk is less than that of catching smallpox in a country where it is known to be prevalent.

Diphtheria immunisation : It is extremely important also to have your child immunised against diphtheria. Immunisation should be completed by the first birthday, so ask about this simple procedure when baby is about six months old.

Baby is usually given two injections, with an interval of four weeks, though some doctors prefer to give three injections in all. Your own doctor will arrange to immunise baby should you wish him to do so, or you can have it done at the nearest Welfare Centre, if you prefer this.

It is not known exactly how long this immunity against diphtheria infection lasts, but it is recommended that children should receive one " booster " injection just before they go to school for the first time, say at four and a half years or even earlier.

Whooping cough immunisation : A combined vaccine which protects the child against both diphtheria and whooping cough can be given, or the whooping cough vaccine can be given separately. Both these procedures mean three injections at monthly intervals.

Scientists are not yet sure how much protection the child will build up as a result of the inoculation. It seems probable that the protective bodies are made slowly, and that whilst the child may still develop whooping cough, the attack will not be so severe. But as whooping cough is such a prevalent disease in built-up areas, and as it is so liable to attack very small children, it is surely a wise plan to do all that is possible to protect the child.

Tetanus immunisation : Tetanus, or lock-jaw, may develop after deep, penetrating wounds contaminated with soil, but it is now possible to prevent this, too, by immunisation. The vaccine may be included with the diphtheria and whooping cough protection, thus reducing the total number of injections.

Tuberculosis vaccination : Any child who is exposed to the risk of tuberculosis infection may be vaccinated with B.C.G. vaccine, in a way rather similar to smallpox vaccination, except that the blister takes much longer to form at the site ; a similar sort of scar remains. At the moment this procedure is carried out at the Chest Clinics run by the Public Health authorities, and enquiries should be made there.

Polio vaccination : Vaccination against poliomyelitis involves two initial injections with three or four weeks between, and a third given several months later. It may be carried out by the Infant Welfare staff or by your own doctor. The procedure is similar to diphtheria immunisation, and leaves no scars.

Treatment for nursery ailments

Colds and Coughs : Small babies are unlikely to catch colds unless they are in direct and close contact with infected people. If you have a cold the germs will not be secreted in your milk, but they come from your nose and throat, so it is wise to wear a mask of butter muslin over your mouth and nose when looking after your baby.

Many babies who are quite normal indulge in a certain amount of sneezing, snorting and snuffling, in their unconscious attempts to keep the air passages clear ; but a running nose, difficulty in breathing through the nose and an unmistakable cough indicate some infection of the respiratory tract. You should get your doctor's advice if baby goes off his food, seems apathetic, looks blue or seems to have difficulty in breathing. But if he is lively, and sucks well in spite of his cold, all that is necessary to overcome his infection is an increase of his vitamin C drink (orange or blackcurrent juice or rosehip syrup) given as warm as he can take it. His nose should be kept clean with wisps of cotton-wool, but drops should be inserted only with your doctor's permission ; they so easily irritate the delicate lining of the nose and make things worse. If his nose is very stuffed and he is disturbed by it at night, it is sometimes helpful to put a little menthol ointment over some Vaseline just under his nose. (Putting anything on the bridge of his nose cannot possibly help.) It is very rarely necessary or effective to give cough medicines to a baby. Anything strong enough to affect the cough will make him sick or too sleepy. If he has bronchitis or a serious chest infection, your doctor will give something much more effective.

Provided he has no temperature and can be kept warm, he is better out of doors with a cold.

Colic : Some quite healthy babies have attacks of screaming and drawing up their legs in pain during the first three months. The popular time for these colicky spasms seems to be the evening. The reason is often obscure, and in many cases frankly no cause can be found. But sometimes it is associated with excessive air swallowing in babies who get too hungry before a feed, or who do not have enough milk, and thus gulp down air instead. But whatever the cause, these attacks seem to do no permanent harm, and the babies grow out of them. The effectiveness of remedies varies, but these have often been found to work :

(*a*) See that the baby is getting enough milk, especially at the early evening feed, and that he has not been kept waiting too long for it.

(*b*) During an actual attack put the baby to lie on his tummy over a warm rubber hot-water bottle (under supervision of course).

(*c*) Give him 1 drop of sal volatile in a teaspoonful of warm water.

Constipation : A bowel movement only every two or three days does not necessarily indicate constipation in young babies. Indeed, after the first few weeks a breast-fed baby often goes as long as four days without passing a stool. It is the character of the stool which indicates whether or not constipation is present. In a breast-fed baby the constipated stool is apt to contain much mucus, and only occurs when the baby is under-fed. Constipation in a bottle-fed baby is more common. In this case the stool is infrequent and hard. Again the cause is underfeeding, and when this is put right the stools will usually become normal again. Until then 1-tea-spoonful doses of liquid paraffin or milk of magnesia may be given. As the baby grows older and takes cereals, strained fruit and vegetables, the stools may become more frequent and more adult in character. Portions of vegetables may be clearly seen in the stools, but unless there is also diarrhœa that is no reason for stopping the particular vegetable.

Convulsions : Babies used to have these more frequently in the last generation than they do now. If you are careful with baby's diet, sleep and general routine, it is unlikely that he will have them at all. But should he suddenly go stiff, lose consciousness, and roll his eyes about, the best treatment is to sponge his head with tepid water, tuck him warmly in bed and send for the doctor.

Crying, excessive : A certain amount of crying is natural, for it is almost the only way in which the baby can express his needs at first. But if he cries continually and seems restless and unhappy, then you must seek the cause.

A frequent cause of such restlessness is feeding difficulty —usually under-feeding—and this possibility must be carefully considered, if necessary with the help of test-feeding. Or there may be something in the baby's routine or general management which needs adjustment. He may be too hot, or bored because left alone too much, or he may not be getting his wind up properly after feeds. Remember he needs to be relaxed over this process, and it is a mistake to try and hurry him, however much you have to do.

But one must also remember that even very young babies vary a good deal in their temperament. Whereas one is placid and contented, another is restless and disturbed. The disturbed baby especially needs the re-assurance of the mother's calm and friendly presence when he is distressed. He should always be handled quietly and confidently ; a nervous or hurried manner will aggravate the difficulty, whereas soothing words and a gentle touch help to calm him. It is a mistake to leave a baby to cry himself into a panic in the hope that he will learn not to cry in future. He will only feel the more insecure and will demand your attention. You can take comfort from the thought that many restless babies grow into lively and intelligent youngsters.

Diarrhœa : A baby, during the first few weeks of his life, usually has frequent motions. They are generally of a mustardy colour and are quite normal. After the first six to eight weeks this gradually settles down, until baby has an average of one or two stools a day.

If it does not settle down, and the stools remain frequent and frothy, and perhaps sometimes green, consider the following possible causes. Is he being made to feel anxious or frustrated ? Are you as calm as you ought to be ? Is he having too much sugar ? Is he being fed too often, for example, at less than three-hour intervals ?

An attack of diarrhœa coming suddenly may mean that baby has taken something that has disagreed with him or poisoned him ; and if the attack is accompanied by vomiting, do not hesitate to send for the doctor.

Digestive difficulty : Abnormal stools containing many white curds show that there is some difficulty in digesting the food, and medical opinion should be sought about modifying the milk in some way. Stools which are large, pale and very offensive indicate that the fats in the food are not being digested, and that there is probably a mild attack of catarrhal jaundice. If the stools are always of this type, further advice should be sought, as it is possible that baby has a permanent inability to deal with all the fats in his food.

Ears : (*a*) *Discharging ears :* Many babies are said by their mothers to have running ears, when the discharge is the natural wax, orange in colour. This of course needs no treatment, and it works itself out in due course. Any material of lighter colour coming from the ear may indicate an infection, and must be immediately reported to your doctor.

(*b*) *Prominent ears :* Many babies lie with their ears crumpled forward, but this rarely has any permanent effect. Protruding ears are usually due to the inborn structure. They generally look less obvious as the child grows and his head begins to fill out behind and his hair gets thicker. If the condition continues to be obvious later on, plastic surgery is the solution, and it is usually done after the child is six or seven. In infancy, strapping the ears back with elastic adhesive plaster may be tried ; if the strapping becomes entangled in the baby's hair, be careful not to pull when removing the plaster, but just cut the hairs concerned. Caps with pads over the ears to hold them in place are not altogether satisfactory : they do not stay in place very well, and are apt to make the baby too hot, especially in summer.

Eyes : (*a*) *Watering and discharging eyes :* It is common for babies' eyes to " water " rather a lot, and usually one is affected more than the other. This condition has nothing whatever to do with the sight and does not denote " weak eyes." It is actually due to a temporary blockage of the nasal duct—the passage which runs from the corner of the eye to the nose as an outlet for the overflow of tears. The diameter of the duct is so small in infants that it is apt to become easily blocked by mucus. It usually opens up spontaneously during the first few months. After the age of nine months or so, or if there is a persistent infection of the eyes, ask your doctor's advice.

A " watery " eye may sometimes appear encrusted with a little dry pus in the morning, indicating a very mild infection. Drops or ointment supplied by your doctor or the Infant Welfare Clinic will quickly clear up this condition.

(b) *Squint :* Nearly all babies squint when they are tiny ; when they grow older they learn to control the eye muscles, and so the squint disappears. If it has not disappeared by the time baby is six to nine months old, it is wise to get advice, as one of his eyes may be defective and he may need treatment.

Hiccups : A short attack of hiccups is common in babies and needs no treatment, but a severe attack after a feed may often be stopped by giving the baby a teaspoonful of warm water containing one drop of sal volatile, or by laying baby on his tummy over a warm (not hot) rubber water-bottle.

Navel hernia : A tag of loose skin over the navel is not a hernia, and will become less obvious in time. But sometimes, the two central muscles of the abdominal wall do not unite properly behind the navel, and through this small opening a rupture or hernia may appear when baby screams or coughs. Crying does not cause the rupture, though it may accentuate it. To treat the condition, it is not sufficient just to push back the rupture with a penny ; the muscles must also be drawn together. From an elastic adhesive bandage, 2 inches wide, cut a strip about 14–16 inches long ; lay baby on the middle part of this, at the level of the navel ; then take hold of the two ends, pull them across baby's tummy and stick down at each side. An extra strip of about 4 inches can be laid across the front of this strapping, just to reinforce the part over the navel.

The baby can be bathed as usual, and the strapping is left on until it loosens spontaneously, after two or three weeks. Then a fresh piece may be applied if necessary. A warning must be given, however, that the strapping may irritate some babies' skins. If so, the effect soon disappears with a soothing cream or Vaseline after the strapping is removed, but it is better not to re-apply it. Remember that these hernias commonly disappear spontaneously, and it is rarely necessary for surgical closure to be considered.

Polyp : During the first few weeks of life the navel may fail to dry up completely, and remains just moist. This " stickiness " is often due to a small red lump or polyp right in the navel. The treatment of this is a simple matter of ligature or the application of a caustic stick, which is quite painless, and which your doctor or the Clinic staff can do for you.

Puffiness of the hands : The hands of small babies often look puffy and blue in cold weather, however warm the rest of the baby may be. This condition is due to a sluggish circulation in the extremities because the small muscles of the hands are not yet being used very much. As the baby grows older and greater activity improves his circulation, the condition disappears.

Scurf (cradle cap) : This accumulation of the natural scalp grease is often increased by oils and ointments mistakenly applied to remove it. To prevent, wash daily with soap and rinse thoroughly ; light friction over the "soft spot" during the shampoo is quite harmless, and indeed beneficial. To clear the scurf, use a weak solution of detergent such as 1 teaspoonful of Cetavlon, Stergene or Teepol to 1 pint of water instead of soap for a day or two. If there is also some reddening of the scalp, consult your doctor.

Skin conditions : The skin of infants is more sensitive than that of older children, so rashes and spots tend to be more common. Most of these are transient, and the treatment is not difficult.

(*a*) *Spots on the face :* During the first few weeks of life, reddish spots are common. If the water in your district is hard, use swabs dipped in liquid paraffin to clean the baby's face.

(*b*) *Heat rash :* Too many clothes and the presence of wool next to the skin may bring out a small rash on baby, which should be treated by reducing the weight of clothing and either lining the vests with silk, or substituting silk and wool vests.

(*c*) *Food rash :* These spots, which occur mostly on the limbs, are few in number, fairly large, raised from the skin surface and look white in the centre. It is the older baby, on a mixed diet, who is more likely to have these. They can be soothed by applying milk of magnesia, which is also useful taken internally in teaspoon doses.

(*d*) *Napkin rash :* A little soreness in the napkin area is almost inevitable at one time or another during babyhood, even in the best cared for child, but a great deal can be done to ensure that it is only transitory and mild. There are several causes of this condition. Loose frequent stools is one, and an improvement can usually be obtained by reducing the amount of sugar if the baby is bottle fed. Inefficient washing and rinsing of the napkins is another common cause. (See " The Baby in the Home," pages 111–112, for notes on the best way of laundering nappies.)

During the teething period soreness is commonly due to irritation by ammonia, liberated from the urine as a result of a chemical reaction between it and traces of soap in the napkins or traces of fæces on the skin. If you detect ammonia, give the baby extra fluids to drink, if he will take them ; take greater care over washing the napkins, as explained above ; change the baby as frequently as you can, consistent with his rest, and when you change him, swab down the sore areas with liquid paraffin to remove the urine from the skin before you put on the clean napkin. At each changing apply a good baby cream or tannic acid jelly or a cream specially sold for this purpose, such as Drapolene. When the weather is warm enough, let baby lie without his napkins pinned on, to allow the air to get to his skin.

If there are open sore areas, report to your doctor for his advice. Never put boracic powder on them, because it may be absorbed and cause general poisoning.

(e) *Infantile eczema :* The treatment of this must always be under your doctor's supervision, but it will be helpful to have the following information.

This condition is not infectious, and does not affect

the general health or development of the baby in the
long run. He will almost always grow out of it at the
end of the teething period, though it may tend to recur
in small patches from time to time after any strain. It
is thought to be a reaction of the skin to some nervous
or physical stress, or to some substance to which the
baby is allergic, for instance certain of the proteins of
cow's milk. (If the latter is suspected, goat's milk or
Allergilac are worth trying.) It is aggravated by heat,
and often by wool worn next to the skin, so a silk or
cotton vest is advisable, and woolly collars at the neck
should be avoided. Keep him as quiet as you can, and
show him a great deal of affection.

Teething : Teething is not necessarily an ailment ; in
fact, some mothers have been surprised to find baby has
cut a tooth even while remaining quite placid. This is
more often the case with the first lower ones. The double
teeth are usually a little more trouble, and baby may be
rather restless at nights and rub his ears a lot. This does
not necessarily mean there is anything wrong with his
ears, but that there is probably a certain amount of
discomfort in the jaw, which is referred back to the ears.
Lancing of the gums is almost never necessary now.
(See pages 101–104, " Causes of Disturbed Sleep.")

Thrush : This is an infection found most commonly
in the mouths of babies, and it may spread if neglected.
It is shown by the presence of whitish spots in the mouth ;
these resemble the remains of milk but cannot of course
be removed when touched. The old remedy of glycerine
and borax has now been abandoned (because of risk of

poisoning) in favour of a gentian violet paint in a half per cent. aqueous solution.

Vomiting and posseting : The majority of babies bring up small amounts of milk after a feed. This may accompany the bringing up of wind, or may be due to jerky handling when they are being changed and dressed afterwards. But some babies indulge in it when lying peacefully in their prams. This kind of vomiting, which is nothing more than a welling up of swallowed milk, is called posseting, and never affects the health of the baby, but if it is a continuous performance it can be a great nuisance to the mother because of the extra washing it involves. A large plastic bib is a great boon in these cases. Posseting is common only during the first three or four months, and usually stops when the feeds are thickened. So in the case of bottle-fed babies it pays to start thickening the milk with cereal earlier than usual.

" Real " vomiting, which is characterised by being in large amounts, or by its great force, or by accompanying diarrhœa, or by being an unusual occurrence for your particular baby, should be reported to your doctor without delay.

Taking a baby's temperature

The most satisfactory place to take your baby's temperature is in the fold of the groin. First shake the thermometer until the mercury is below the 95° mark, then place the thermometer in the groin, flex the thigh up over the abdomen and keep in position for at least two minutes.

Remember that a child may " run a temperature " for very little, and that in any case its average temperature is half a degree higher than that of an adult.

Nursery accidents

The parents of young children should do all they can to avoid the occurrence of accidents in their homes. Little children and babies are quite defenceless, and the effect of even a small burn or scald can be threatening to life because of the profound shock which follows.

There are certain safety-first measures which should be taken, although they may mean some outlay of money and time ; they are particularly necessary when baby becomes mobile.

Indoor precautions

(*a*) In all rooms where a baby is left, a first essential is a properly secured fireguard ; this should completely enclose the fire, and be of the mesh type (supplementing the bars which are normally fixed to a gas or electric fire).

(*b*) Electric fitments (especially portable fires) are best placed out of reach. Sockets of electric switches should be the shuttered type. (If you have difficulty in buying these, consult your electricity showrooms.)

(*c*) All matches should be kept out of sight and reach.

(*d*) When baby reaches the crawling stage make sure that the top of the stairs is adequately shut off, either by fixing a small gate or by using a barrier, such as the folded playpen. Any window which the child can reach should be guarded.

(e) All teapots, jugs, pans and kettles containing hot liquid must be placed in the centre of the table, well away from baby's farthest reach. Tablecloths should not overhang the edge of the table when baby is about.

(f) Handles of pots and pans on the stove must be turned inwards.

(g) Put any precious or harmful object right away, so that you avoid too many commands of the "don't touch" variety. All babies go through a stage when they instinctively put every object they can reach into the mouth. Be constantly on the watch, and see that any small interesting objects, such as safety-pins, buttons, money, etc., are not left lying around.

(h) Medicines and pills, especially attractively coloured ones, should be locked away.

(i) All cleaning materials, such as bottles of bleach, packets of soap powder and detergent, floor polish and metal polish, should be put high out of reach.

Outdoor precautions

(a) Have a secure fastening to the garden gate.

(b) See that there is a secure lid or covering to any tub or container of water.

(c) Make sure that the pram has safe brakes and that it is properly balanced.

(d) A piece of netting to fix across the pram is a useful protection against intruding cats or even dogs.

First-aid Box

It is useful to have a few first-aid remedies kept in readiness in case accidents occur. These should include :—

Cotton-wool	Antiseptic solution, e.g.
White lint	Dettol or Savlon
Bandages	Antiseptic cream, e.g.
Scissors	a cetrimide preparation
Bicarbonate of soda	Adhesive dressings
Calamine lotion	Pair of fine tweezers

Abrasions and cuts : Wash well with clean water and soap, adding a little antiseptic lotion if necessary.

An abrasion is best left without a dressing, unless it is very deep, because a protective scab forms if it is left dry. Should the abrasion be deep, dress with some lint spread with a little antiseptic cream.

An open cut is often best treated with an adhesive dressing, which should be left in place as long as possible, and kept dry. If the cut gapes widely, do not hesitate to get your doctor to see it, as a stitch may be necessary.

Burns and scalds : With a small one, hold the part in a solution of bicarbonate of soda (1 tsp. to 1 pint), then cover with lint, and bandage it. Do not remove the blister, as this forms a protective covering. Later, when the blister bursts, cut away the dead skin and dress again.

If the area is at all large, you must call the doctor or take the child to hospital, as there are often quite severe after-effects. If such medical aid is almost immediately available, it is better to leave the burnt area severely alone, except to cover it with something freshly laundered,

such as a sheet, pillow-case or large handkerchief. But
if you are in an isolated spot with no medical aid for
miles, cover the burns and scalds with a clean dressing
(gauze or freshly laundered linen) soaked in a solution
of bicarbonate of soda in the proportion of 1 teaspoonful
to a pint of warm water. The child should meanwhile
be kept as quiet as possible, and given plenty to drink.

Bruises : These rarely require any treatment, as they
merely indicate bleeding beneath the skin, which is self-
limiting. Encourage baby to ignore bumps and bruises
as much as possible.

Head injuries : Even the best-cared-for baby will
sometimes bump his head. If his colour remains good
and he stops crying within 10–15 minutes and does not
vomit, you can be sure that he has not injured his brain
in any way. Should he lose consciousness, or vomit or
become pale and restless, let a doctor see him at once.

After any fall involving a blow on the head it is a wise
plan to let the child rest quietly in bed for an hour or two.

Swallowed objects and choking : Children may swallow
such objects as buttons, safety-pins, coins and fruit
stones. Usually these objects pass quite naturally through
the body and can be seen in the child's motions within
2 or 3 days. If during this time he shows signs of
abdominal pain and vomits, you will have to send for
the doctor. Should the object be sharp or pointed, take
the child to see a doctor or to a hospital at once.

If baby gets anything stuck in his throat and starts to
choke, pat him on the back and if necessary pick him up
by his feet, hold him upside down and then pat his back

quite sharply. If you cannot dislodge the object in this way, you must rush him off to hospital or to your doctor, as there is no time to lose.

Organisations for Handicapped Children

British Asthma Association, 11 Chandos Street, W.1.

British Diabetic Association, 152 Harley Street, W.1.

British Epilepsy Association, 27 Nassau Street, W.1.

Central Council for the Care of Cripples, 34 Eccleston Square, S.W.1.

Deaf Children's Society, 1 Macklin Street, W.C.2.

Rubella Children Parents' Group, (sec. Mrs. Peggy Freeman), 63 Horn Lane, Woodford Green, Essex.

Hæmophilia Society, 94 Southwark Bridge Road, S.E.1.

Infantile Paralysis Fellowship, Rugby Chambers, Great James Street, W.C.1.

Muscular Dystrophy Group run by the Central Council for the Care of Cripples (see above).

National Institute for the Deaf, 105 Gower Street, W.C.1.

National Association for Mental Health, 39 Queen Anne Street, W.1.

National Society for Mentally Handicapped Children Ltd., 162A Strand, W.C.2.

National Spastics Society, 28 Fitzroy Square, W.1.

Royal National Institute for the Blind, 224 Great Portland Street, W.1.

Adopting a Baby

There are very many happily married couples who are most anxious to have a family, but who, for medical reasons, are unable to achieve it naturally. The way is still open to them to complete their family by adopting a child (or more than one). If you are in this position, you will want to know the special considerations to be taken into account and the procedure to be followed.

Before you decide to adopt a baby, you should give most careful thought to the matter. Remember that the only really valid reason for wanting to take a child into your family is because you want him for himself, just as he is and will be—not only a baby to fill your arms, but an active toddler, a noisy schoolboy, a lanky teen-ager— in fact, a human being in his own right.

Adoption should ideally be a joint affair, so talk the whole matter over thoroughly with your husband. Only if you are both fully agreed that you want to have an adopted baby is the venture likely to be a real success.

It is best to adopt a young baby wherever possible. Don't try to take a short cut and avoid the nappy-washing, hoping to have a " ready-made," nicely trained little child. The baby needs a continuous relationship with one loving mother and the earlier this can begin (subject to legal provisos), the better for him and for you. It is through the physical care and handling you give him while he is helpless that the bonds of love will be forged between you.

A possible exception is in the case of an older foster-child, who may have lived in your home until he seemed like one of the family. In that case a later adoption may work very happily.

Planning the adoption

You will want to make as certain as you reasonably can that the baby's physical and mental heritage have been fully investigated. It is at least equally important that you and your husband should be in good health and of suitable temperaments to undertake this important responsibility. The thorough investigation needed is best ensured if the adoption is carried out by a registered adoption society or by the Children's Department of a County Council or County Borough. There are over fifty registered adoption societies in the country, a few of them working on a national basis, some as departments of the well-known Children's Societies, others on a local scale. Some have religious affiliations and require the applicants to be of the same faith, others, while non-denominational, require applicants to be of some religion. Adoption societies do not charge fees for their services.

There are at present many more applicants than there are children available for adoption. If your application is accepted, you may have to wait some considerable time before a suitable baby is offered to you. There are a number of reasons for this : the majority of the children in public care have relatives and they are not available for adoption ; many unmarried mothers keep their babies, and it is desirable that they should do so whenever it is possible ; in other cases, babies are not considered suitable for adoption on account of some physical or mental handicap.

It is unwise to form too exact a picture of the type of child you want. Every effort will be made to match the baby who is offered to you to your personal circumstances—for the rest, keep an open mind.

The rules governing adoption are laid down by law, and in addition, the adoption societies may have regulations of their own. Applicants, or one of them in the case of a couple, must be not less than 25 years old and not less than 21 years older than the child (the legal term in this context is " the infant "), though there is an exception to this if the adopters are near relatives of the child. They must be resident and domiciled in the United Kingdom.

The baby arrives

In time, if all is satisfactory, the adoption society will let you know that they can offer a suitable child to you. If, when you have seen him, you honestly feel that you can take him to your heart, he will be given to you. Allow yourself and the baby a little time to settle down together. Then, having decided that you really hope to adopt him, you must notify the Children's Officer at the Town or County Hall of your intention to apply for an Adoption Order. From that date begins the three months' probationary period, which is the legal time given for official investigations.

Your next step is to obtain the necessary forms of application from the Juvenile Court or the County Court. The adoption society will help you to complete them and will obtain the consents to the adoption. The mother cannot give a valid consent to the adoption of her child until he is six weeks old, and it is usually wise not to take a baby into your home for adoption until that consent has been given. Once it has been given, and you have lodged your application, the mother cannot remove the baby from your care without the Court's consent.

During the three months' probationary period, you will be visited in your home by an officer of the Court, who is specially appointed to safeguard the child's interests, and also very probably by a Health Visitor, who will be able to give you valuable advice about the baby's care.

A date will be fixed by the Court for the hearing of the case, which is held in private. You will not see the child's parents or relatives and your name can be kept confidential.

Once the Order is made, the child will be a full legal member of your family. The original birth certificate is returned, to be replaced by an Adoption Certificate. (A shortened form of certificate does not disclose the fact of adoption.) You can have any new names you may have chosen entered on the Order, but if the child has already been baptised, he cannot be re-baptised with new names. He can inherit in the same way as children born to you, except in the case of a title or an entailed estate, but he will not inherit under a will made before the Order. It is therefore important to make a new will including the adopted child.

There are a number of practical matters about which you will want information. Once your application has been accepted, it is a very wise plan to use the waiting time in the same way as you would if a baby were to be born to you, in learning mothercraft. You can usually arrange to spend some time at a local day nursery, where you could help to bath and feed the small babies, and you might join a mothercraft class in your district.

Clothes for the baby

When you actually know that you are bringing home a baby, you will have to get clothes and equipment ready without very much time for preparation. Find out first what will be provided when he comes to you. Remember, too, that the adoption is not complete until the Order is made. Your preparations, therefore, while they should of course be fully adequate, should not be over-elaborate.

Assuming that the baby will be six weeks old when he comes to you, he will need :

4 gowns	2 dozen towelling napkins
4 vests	2 dozen gauze napkins
3 matinee jackets	Bonnet and mitts for a
4 pairs bootees	winter baby.

As the baby will be bottle fed, you should ask the Health Visitor's advice about feeding methods before the baby arrives and study the information given in this book. Hold him closely and give him plenty of mothering at feeding times.

The adopted child in the home

It will doubtless be pointed out to you before you have the baby how necessary it is to tell him that he is adopted. You can do this in the most natural way if you talk to him about his adoption, right from the time he can talk. Tell him that you chose him when he was a baby, to be yours for ever, because you loved him. When he asks about his original mother, as he is bound to do one day, you can quite truthfully say that you know very little about her, but tell him that she loved him too, and was anxious for him to have a good home where he could grow up happily. Don't delay in talking about this subject or try to hide it. It would only make for insincerity between you and your child, and it would break his trust in you if he felt you had ever deceived him. He will grow deeply into your family through the years even without a blood bond.

Later on you may hope to adopt a second and even a third child, spacing them in a natural way.

It does sometimes happen that after a child has been adopted, a baby is born naturally into the family. If this should happen, all the better ; if you love children for their own sake, you will have plenty of room in your heart for all of them.

Patterns for the Layette

In this chapter will be found full instructions for making all the first-year garments shown in Plates XIII–XVI, and those for the second year shown in Plates XVII–XX.

Gown and Raglan Jacket

Materials : 2 yds. 36-inch material ; 1 yd. narrow ribbon ; 1 card bias binding ; 1 skein each of pink, blue, yellow and green stranded cotton ; 7 small buttons.

Pattern : Make a full-size paper pattern, following diagrams on pages 209 and 210.

Cutting : Place pattern on material, following layout chart below. $\frac{3}{8}$-inch seam turnings have been allowed, 1 inch for gown and jacket hems, $\frac{1}{2}$ inch for gown and jacket sleeve hems. Cut out.

Marking out : Mark the following with tacking :

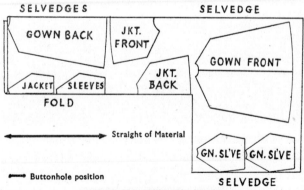

LAYOUT FOR GOWN AND JACKET

centre front and back lines and dotted lines ; position
of buttonholes and tapes.

To make up the Gown : Join raglan, side and sleeve
seams, making narrow flat seams. Turn up bottom
hem and sleeve hems. Neaten neck with bias binding.
Turn in centre back edges on dotted line and neaten.
Work three buttonholes as marked on right back and
sew buttons on left back along centre line. Sew two
6-inch lengths of ribbon on neck edges of back opening ;
one ribbon is stitched to inside of the right neck edge,
the other $\frac{1}{2}$ inch from the left neck edge on the outside.
Make two small buttonholes on each sleeve where
indicated in diagram. Sew bias binding round inside

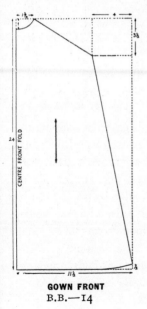

GOWN FRONT
B.B.—14

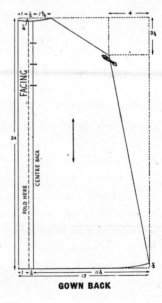

GOWN BACK

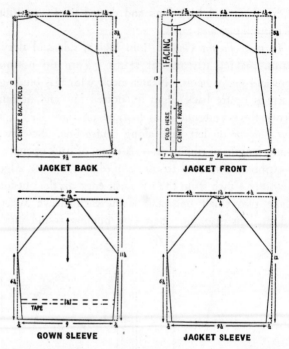

JACKET BACK   JACKET FRONT

GOWN SLEEVE   JACKET SLEEVE

of sleeves in position marked " Tape " (covering button-holes on inside). Thread one 12-inch length of ribbon through bias binding on each sleeve to act as draw-string.

To make up the Matinee Jacket : Join raglan, side and sleeve seams, making narrow flat seams. Turn up bottom hem and sleeve hems. Neaten with bias binding. Turn in centre front edges along dotted line. Make buttonholes as indicated and sew on buttons.

Embroidery : This is the same on both gown and jacket. Trace the design (see page 212) on the fronts parallel to front raglan seams, starting about $\frac{3}{8}$ inch from neck edge. Work stems and bluebells in stem-stitch; daisies and leaves in lazy-daisy; centres and buds in French knots, using green for all stems and leaves, blue, pink and yellow for flowers.

Baby's Petticoat

Materials: $\frac{1}{2}$ yd. 36-inch material; 1 yd. bias binding; 1 small button.

Pattern: Make a full-size paper pattern, following diagram below.

Cutting: Cut out, allowing $\frac{3}{8}$-inch seam turnings. Cut $3\frac{1}{2}$-inch centre back opening.

To make up: Join shoulder and side seams, making narrow flat seams. Neaten neck, arm-holes and neck opening with bias binding. Make loop for button on right neck edge and sew on button. Finish low hem.

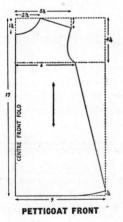

PETTICOAT FRONT

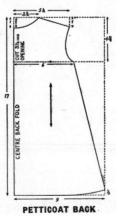

PETTICOAT BACK

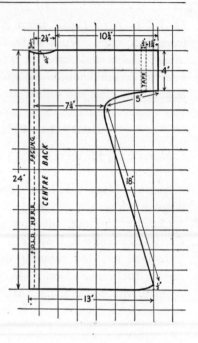

EMBROIDERY DIAGRAM
(ACTUAL SIZE)

Magyar-type Gown

This may be used for either day or night wear for the first few months.

Materials: $1\frac{1}{3}$ yds. 27-inch material (4 yds. for 3 gowns); $\frac{3}{4}$ yd. narrow ribbon; 3 small buttons.

Make paper pattern from diagram above. When cutting out, place centre front to a fold, and centre back (which is left open) to a selvedge. Turn in to face selvedge edges and make buttonholes. Make up in same way as raglan gown.

Clothes for the Second Year

From here to page 222 are patterns and instructions for the basic garments your child needs as he outgrows his baby clothes. They comprise a simple dress and panties, which can be adapted to make rompers for a boy, a blouse and dungarees, which can be made with short legs. Instructions for a knitted twin set begin on page 252.

DRESS AND PANTIES PATTERNS

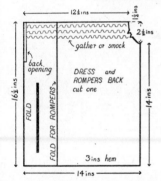
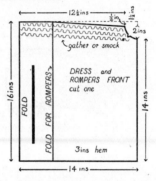

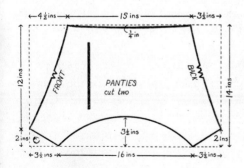

See page 221 for key to the symbols used in these pattern diagrams.

DRESS ANG PANTIES PATTERNS (continued)

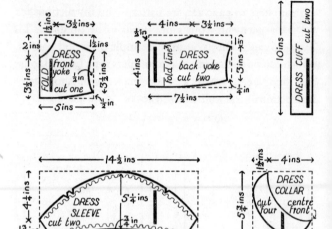

Dress and Panties

Materials : 2 yards 36-inch material ; bias binding for neck edge ; 2 press studs ; elastic for knickers ; sewing cotton.

Pattern and cutting : Make a full-size paper pattern from the diagrams (page 213) and place the pieces on the material according to the cutting layout. Cut out, noting that $\frac{3}{8}$-inch turnings and a 3-inch hem have been allowed for the dress, and $\frac{3}{4}$-inch hems for the knickers, but allow more for turnings if your fabric frays easily.

CUTTING LAYOUT FOR DRESS AND PANTIES

First cut dress pieces (below), then open fabric and cut remaining parts (right).

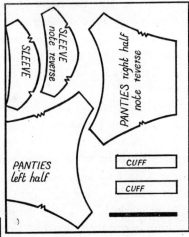

SLEEVE

SLEEVE note reverse

PANTIES right half note reverse

PANTIES left half

CUFF

CUFF

open out one yard of fabric to full width

back yoke

collar

collar

front yoke

FRONT DRESS & ROMPERS

straight of fabric

fold for rompers

BACK DRESS & ROMPERS

fold for rompers

$\frac{3}{8}$ths seam allowance

FOLD FOR DRESS

To make these as a boy's romper suit, cut your paper pattern at line marked " Fold for rompers " on dress front and back, and put this edge to the fabric fold when cutting out.

bind back opening turn right lap inside

To make up : Gather front of dress where indicated on diagram, also the back, at each side of opening. Neaten 4-inch back opening with binding. Join front to front yoke. Join back to the two back yoke pieces, placing the bound edge of the back opening to the fold line of the back yoke facing. Next join the shoulder seams.

Place each pair of collar pieces together, right sides facing, machine round outside edges, and turn right side out. Tack collars in position, one very slightly overlapping the other at the centre front, and stitch to neck edge. Clip neck edge and collar, and bind down raw edges with bias binding. Turn in back yoke facings at point marked " fold line " on pattern.

Using largest stitch, machine along top and bottom of sleeves as indicated on diagram, then pull up threads, gathering sleeves to fit armhole and cuff band respectively. Join lower edge of sleeves to cuff strips, and pin top edge of sleeves to armholes, matching notches, then machine. Join underarm and side seams. Turn cuff edges under, and slip-stitch on wrong side. Turn up a 3-inch hem along bottom of frock. Sew on press studs at back opening.

Panties : Join centre front and back seams, and join inner leg seams. Clip all curves, and press seams open. Make a $\frac{3}{4}$-inch hem at waist and legs. Cut elastic 2 inches shorter at waist and 1 inch shorter at leg than pattern measurements, thread it into place, and sew the ends firmly together.

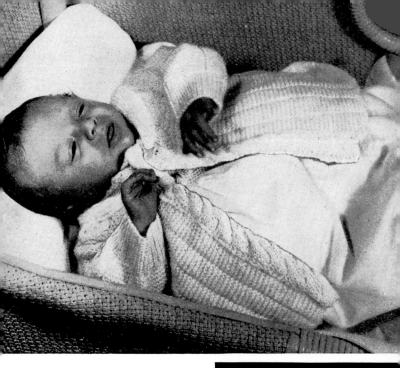

Plate XIII

BABY'S LAYETTE

Here and in the next three pages are pictures of coats, vests, gowns, etc., to knit or make : full directions are given at the end of the book. The matinée jacket seen above may be worn reversed (see small picture), to prevent it becoming too damp. For full lists of all the clothes which are needed, see the chapter, " Baby's Layette and Equipment."

In cold weather, all but the tiniest babies need a pram suit. This practical set has a jacket with snugly-fitting collar and capacious leggings, and has an alternative bonnet and cap with ear-flaps to suit either a girl or boy. Bands of contrasting colour make a pretty finish. Mitts are essential in winter-time to keep baby's hands from becoming chilled. To wear indoors, baby will also need cosy tie-on bootees. (See above.)

Plate XV

The first-size cardigan above is made with sensible, roomy raglan sleeves, to go over dresses. Equally practical are the rompers, which are suitable for either a girl or a boy, and which open easily for nappy-changing. We give instructions for alternative vest patterns, and choice is a matter for personal preference. A pilch helps to keep the nappies in place when baby gets more active, and looks neat under a short dress.

Plate XVI

For the first few months, baby wears a gown day and night. Here is a practical raglan type, with a matching jacket, and a neat petticoat to wear under a thin dress on colder days. The unusual " hug-me-tight " illustrated on the left is excellent for a very tiny baby.

Romper Suit

This is made exactly as for the dress and panties, but the top may be cut 2 inches shorter, and the fullness may be reduced by 16 inches (i.e., make front and back each 20 inches wide, instead of previous measurement); cut the back and front skirt pieces at the line marked "fold for rompers," and place this edge to fold of material.

If the material has a " one-way only " design, take care to get this the same way up on both parts of knickers.

BLOUSE PATTERNS

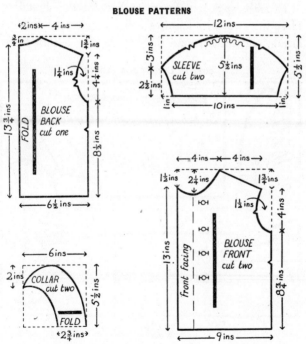

Blouse

Materials: $\frac{5}{8}$ yard 36-inch material; 4 buttons; $\frac{1}{2}$ yard bias binding; sewing cotton.

Pattern and cutting: Make a full-size paper pattern from the diagrams (page 217), and place the pieces on the material according to the cutting layout. Cut out, noting that $\frac{3}{8}$ inch has been allowed for turnings, but allow more if your material frays easily; $\frac{1}{2}$-inch hems have been allowed.

To make up: Join fronts to back at the shoulders. Place the two thicknesses of collar together, right sides facing, and stitch round the outside edge; turn collar

CUTTING LAYOUT FOR BLOUSE

SLEEVE

straight of fabric
BLOUSE
front

collar

BLOUSE
back

FOLD

right side out, and sew to neck edge of blouse. Neaten inside neck with bias binding. Turn in front facings and neaten top edges. Machine along top of sleeve between notches, using largest stitch, and draw up the thread slightly, until the sleeve fits the armhole, then sew it in position.

Join underarm sleeve seams and side seams. Turn up $\frac{1}{2}$-inch hems at lower edge of sleeves. Make a narrow hem at bottom of blouse. Work buttonholes, and sew on buttons.

Dungarees

Materials : $1\frac{1}{4}$ yds. 36-inch material ; 4 buttons ; sewing cotton.

Pattern and cutting : Make a full-size paper pattern from the diagrams (page 220), and place the pieces on the material according to the cutting layout. Cut out, noting that $\frac{3}{8}$ inch has been allowed for turnings (but allow more if your fabric frays easily) ; $2\frac{1}{2}$-inch hems have been allowed for the legs.

To make up : Join front seams marked ∧∧∧, clip at curve, and press open. Join back seams marked ∧∧, clip at curve and press open. Join inside leg seams. Next join both the side seams below the side openings. Turn up a $2\frac{1}{2}$-inch hem at bottom of each leg. (This may be turned up as a cuff, and let down as the child grows.) Join the two halves of the back facing, turn in a narrow single hem, and machine. Place facings on dungaree back, right side of fabric facing, and stitch

(*Turn to page* 222)

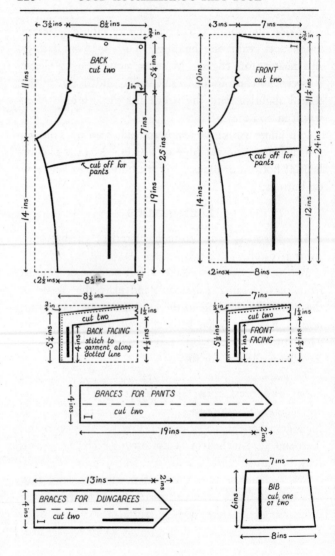

← 3½ ins → ← 8½ ins →   ← 3 ins → ← 7 ins →

BACK
cut two

FRONT
cut two

11 ins

5¼ ins

1 in

7 ins

25 ins

cut off for
pants

19 ins

← 2½ ins × 8½ ins →

10 ins

14 ins

11¼ ins

24 ins

cut off for
pants

12 ins

‹2 ins› 8 ins →

← 8½ ins →   ← 7 ins →

cut two   1½ ins

5¼ ins   4 ins   4½ ins

BACK FACING
stitch to
garment along
dotted line

cut two   1½ ins

5¼ ins   4 ins   4½ ins

FRONT
FACING

BRACES FOR PANTS

4 ins   cut two

← 19 ins → × 2 →

BRACES FOR DUNGAREES

← 13 ins → × 2 →

4 ins   cut two

← 7 ins →

BIB
cut one
or two

6 ins

← 8 ins →

CUTTING LAYOUT FOR DUNGAREES

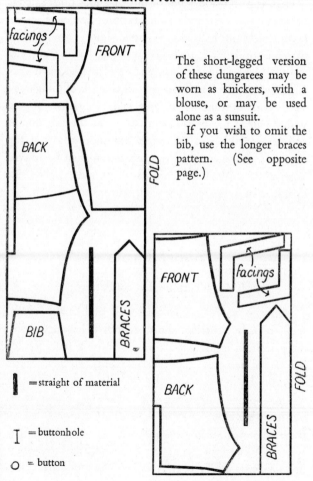

The short-legged version of these dungarees may be worn as knickers, with a blouse, or may be used alone as a sunsuit.

If you wish to omit the bib, use the longer braces pattern. (See opposite page.)

▮	= straight of material
I	= buttonhole
○	= button

along top edge ; clip close to stitching, and turn facing inside. Face front of dungarees in same way.

Hem top and side edges of bib, and join bottom edge to wrong side of trouser front, turning raw edge under. Fold braces in half along dotted line, right side of material inside, and stitch round edges, leaving one end open ; turn right side out, and sew up the open end. Cross braces and join slanting ends to back of dungarees, then work buttonholes in free end of braces. If you wish to have the braces adjustable, cut the bib double and after making it up, work buttonholes at the top corners : the buttons on the braces can then be moved as required. Work buttonholes where indicated on side openings of dungarees. Sew all buttons in position.

Short Pants

(Made from Dungarees Pattern)

Allow $\frac{3}{4}$ yard 36-inch material, and make as for dungarees, but cut legs short, as shown by curved line on pattern diagram, and turn up only 1 inch for leg hems. If desired, omit the bib, and lengthen braces accordingly.

These pants look better with the long braces when worn with a blouse ; if, however, they are intended for use as a sun or play suit, and will be worn without a blouse, it is probably better to retain the bib, which helps to keep the braces in place on the shoulders.

Knitted Patterns

(See Plates XIII–XV)

Abbreviations for Knitting.—Alt. = alternate ; beg. = beginning ; cont. = continue ; d.c. = double crochet ; dec. = decrease ; inc. = increase ; ins. = inches ; k. = knit ; m. 1 = make 1 (i.e., increase) ; p. = purl; patt. = pattern ; p.s.s.o. = pass slipped st. over knitted st. ; rem. = remaining ; rep. = repeat ; r.s. = right side ; sl. = slip ; st. = stitch ; t.b.l. = through back of loop ; tog. = together ; w.f. = wool forward ; w.s. = wrong side ; garter st. = garter stitch (knit every row) ; m. st. = moss stitch (1st row : k.1, p.1 ; 2nd row : k. the p. sts. and p. the k. sts.) ; st. st. = stocking stitch (k. 1 row, p. 1 row) ; instructions in brackets ( ) to be repeated the stated number of times.

Button-through Vest

Materials : 1¼ oz. 3-ply baby wool, one pair of No. 10 knitting-needles, 3 buttons.

Measurements : Length, 10½ ins. ; width all round when buttoned, 15 ins.

Tension : 8 sts. and 10 rows (very slightly stretched) to 1 in. on No. 10 needles.

Back : Cast on 61 sts. Work in rib as follows : *1st row :* P. 1, (K. 2, p. 1) 20 times. *2nd row :* K.1, (p. 2, k. 1) 20 times. This is the pattern used throughout. Cont. until work measures 7¼ ins. Cast on 3 sts. at beg. of next 12 rows (97 sts.). Cont. without further shaping until work measures 10½ ins. Cast off.

Right Front : Cast on 48 sts. and work as follows : K. 5, patt. to end. *2nd row :* Patt. 43, k. 5. Cont. in this way until work measures $7\frac{1}{4}$ ins., making a buttonhole (k. 1, k. 2 tog., m. 1, k. 2) at $4\frac{1}{4}$ ins., $6\frac{3}{4}$ ins. and $9\frac{1}{4}$ ins. When work measures $7\frac{1}{4}$ ins., cast on 3 sts. at beg. of next 6 w.s. rows (66 sts.). Cont. on these sts. until work measures $9\frac{1}{4}$ ins. immediately after third buttonhole. Cast off 16, then rib to end of row (50 sts.). Take 2 tog. at neck edge on next 10 rows (40 sts.). Cont. until work measures $10\frac{3}{4}$ ins. Cast off rem. 40 sts.

Left Front : Work to match right front, reversing all shapings and omitting buttonholes.

To make up : Join shoulder seams. Join side seams. Sew on buttons and work a little crochet fancy edging round neck and sleeves as follows : Work 2 rows double crochet, then work (1 d.c., 2 treble, 1 d.c. into next st., miss 1 st.) to end. Fasten off.

Ribbed Vest

Materials : $1\frac{1}{4}$ oz. 3-ply baby wool, one pair of No. 10 knitting-needles, 2 buttons.

Measurements : Length, $10\frac{1}{2}$ ins. ; chest, 15 ins.

Tension : 8 sts. and 10 rows, (slightly stretched) to 1 in.

Front : Cast on 62 sts. Work in rib of k. 1, p. 1 for $6\frac{1}{2}$ ins. *Next row :* Rib 28 and leave on spare needle, k. 6. rib 28. Cont. on these 34 sts., always knitting central 6 sts., for $1\frac{1}{4}$ ins. Now, beg. at central edge, k. 2, k. 2 tog., m. 1, k. 1, rib to end. Work a further $1\frac{1}{2}$ ins., then make a second buttonhole. When work measures $9\frac{1}{2}$ ins., r.s. facing, k. 8 sts. and place on safety-pin, rib to end. Take 2 tog. at neck edge on next 10 rows. Work 3 rows. Cast off. Now cast on 6 sts., then, beg. at centre, work back on 28 sts. from spare needle. Work up to match first shoulder, but omitting buttonholes.

Back : With No. 10 needles, cast on 62 sts. Work in rib for $10\frac{1}{2}$ ins. Cast off.

Sleeve : Cast on 32 sts. and rib for 2 ins., inc. at both ends of 5th and every following 4th row until there are 40 sts. on needle. When work measures 2 ins., cast off.

To make up : Press very lightly. Join shoulder seams. Set in sleeves, join side seams. Sew on buttons and neaten fastening. Take 8 sts. from safety-pin on right front, pick up 15 sts. from right front and 30 sts. from back of neck and 15 sts. from left front, take 8 sts. from safety-pin on left front. Work 6 rows garter-st. Cast off.

Matinee Coat

Materials : $2\frac{1}{4}$ oz. 3-ply baby wool, one pair each of Nos. 10 and 11 knitting-needles, 3 buttons.

Measurements : Length, $11\frac{1}{2}$ ins. ; chest, 19 ins. ; underarm seam, 6 ins. This garment is reversible and can be worn with the fastening up either back or front.

Tension : 8 sts. and 10 rows to 1 in. in patt.

Front : With No. 10 needles, cast on 106 sts. and work in patt. as follows : *1st row :* (P. 1, k. 6) 15 times, p. 1. *2nd row :* K.

B.B.—15

These 2 rows complete the patt. and are used through-out body of work. Cont. until work measures $7\frac{1}{2}$ ins. *Next row* (r.s.) : K. 2 tog. twice (k. 2, k. 2 tog.) 25 times, k. 2 tog. (78 sts.). Change to garter-st. and k. back. Cast off 2 sts. at beg. of next 2 rows. *Next row* (r.s.) : K. 2 tog., k. 28, cast off 14, k. 28, k. 2 tog. K. back on 29 sts. Cast off 5 sts. at beg. of next r.s. row and take 2 tog. at end. Cast off 4 sts. at beg. of next 2 r.s. rows, take 2 tog. at end. Cast off 3 sts. at beg. of next 3 r.s. rows and take 2 tog. at end. Pull last st. through on last row. Work second shoulder to match, reversing all shapings.

Right Back : With No. 10 needles cast on 56 sts. and work as follows, making body of coat in patt. with 6 sts. st.-st. cable at edge. *1st row :* K. 6, patt. 50. *2nd row :* Patt. 50, p. 6. Rep. these 2 rows. *5th row :* Place 3 sts. on spare needle and leave at back of work, k. 3, k. 3 from spare needle, patt. 50. Rep. 2nd row. Rep. 1st and 2nd rows. These 8 rows complete the patt. and are used throughout body of work. Cont. until work measures $7\frac{1}{2}$ ins. Work a buttonhole (k. 2, k. 2 tog., m. 1, k. 2) on 5th row of cable at $7\frac{1}{2}$ ins., $8\frac{3}{4}$ ins. and 10 ins. After working first buttonhole, at $7\frac{1}{2}$ ins., and with r.s. of work facing, k. 6 sts. of border, then k. 2 tog. (k. 2, k. 2 tog.) 12 times (43 sts.). Change to garter st. and k. back. Cast off 2 sts. at beg. of next row at arm-hole edge. *Next row :* K. 13 and leave on spare needle, k. to end, knitting last 2 sts. tog. Cast off 5 sts. at beg. of next r.s. row and take 2 tog. at end. Cast off 4 sts. at beg. of next 2 r.s. rows and take 2 tog.

at end. Cast off 3 sts. at beg. of next r.s. rows and take 2 tog. at end, pulling last st. of last row through.

Left Back : Work to match right back, reversing all shapings and omitting buttonholes.

Sleeves (both alike) : With No. 11 needles, cast on 50 sts. and work 1½ ins. in rib. Change to No. 10 needles and patt. and cont. until work measures 6 ins. Cast off 2 sts. at beg. of next 2 rows, then take 2 tog. at each end of next 7 rows (32 sts.). Leave on spare needle.

Yoke : Press all pieces lightly under damp cloth. Join sleeves to body. Now with No. 10 needles take 13 sts. from spare needle on right back, pick up 18 sts. from rest of right back, 32 from right sleeve, 42 from front, 32 from left sleeve, 18 from rest of left back and 13 from spare needle of left back (168 sts.). *1st row :* P. 6 (k. 3, p. 6) 17 times, k. 3, p. 6. *2nd row :* K. 6 (p. 3, k. 6) 17 times, p. 3, k. 6. Rep. 1st row. Cable on each set of 6 sts. on next row, then rep. 1st and 2nd rows, then rep. 1st row. Now cont. to work 6 sts. for cable at both ends of row, and work rest of yoke in garter st. as follows : *Next row* (1st dec. row) : Work 6 k. sts. for border, k. 2 (k. 2 tog., k. 3) 30 times, k. 2 tog., k. 2. K. 6 for border (137 sts.). K. 7 rows. *2nd dec. row :* K. 6 for border, k. 2 (k. 2 tog., k. 2) 30 times, k. 2 tog., k. 1, k. 6 for border (106 sts.). Work 3 rows. *3rd dec. row :* K. 6 for border, k. 2, (k. 2 tog., k. 1) 30 times, k. 2 tog., k. 6 for border (75 sts.). Work 6 rows. Cast off.

To make up : Join sleeve and side seams. Sew on buttons. Work small crochet edging round neck.

Baby's Hug-me-tight

Materials : 2 oz. 3-ply baby wool ; 1 pair each Nos. 11 and 12 knitting needles ; 2 buttons.

Measurements : Length, 7 ins. ; chest, 20 ins. ; sleeve seam (with cuff turned back), 5 ins.

Tension : 8 sts. to 1 in., measured over moss st.

Note.—The body and sleeves of this cardigan are knitted all in one piece.

With No. 12 needles, cast on 66 sts. Work 10 rows in k. 1, p. 1 rib, inc. at end of last row.

Change to No. 11 needles and m. st., inc. at both ends of 4th, 8th, 12th, 16th and 18th rows (77 sts.).

Inc. at beg. of next 4 rows ; cast on 2 sts. at beg. of next 4 rows (89 sts.) ; cast on 4 sts. at beg. of next 10 rows (129 sts.).

Work 3¼ ins. without shaping.

Next row : Work 50, cast off 29, work to end. Work 3¼ ins. on last 50 sts., inc. at neck edge of every 4th row without shaping at sleeve end. Cont. inc. at neck edge of every 4th row, and on the rows beg. at sleeve end work as follows : cast off 4 sts. 5 times, cast off 2 sts. twice, dec. twice, dec. on every 4th row 3 times. Work 4 rows without shaping at side seam.

Change to No. 12 needles and work 4 rows in k. 1, p. 1 rib.

5th row.—Rib 18, w.f., k. 2 tog., rib to end. Work 4 rows in rib. Cast off in rib.

Join wool at shoulder and work other side to match, reversing all shapings and omitting buttonhole.

With No. 12 needles, pick up and k. 40 sts. along end
of sleeve, work $2\frac{1}{4}$ ins. in k. 1, p. 1 rib.   Cast off in rib.
Work other sleeve to match.   Join side seams.

Neck band : With No. 12 needles, cast on 7 sts.

1st row : (K. 1, p. 1) twice, k. 1, w.f., k. 2 tog.   *2nd
row :* K. 1, w.f., k. 2 tog. (k. 1, p. 1) twice.   Rep. last
2 rows.   Rep. 1st row.

6th row : K. 1 (w.f., k. 2 tog.) twice, k. 1, p. 1.   Rep.
1st and 2nd rows until strip measures 18 ins.   Sew strip
round neck edge, with openwork edge to edge of
garment.

Sew on buttons.   Press lightly.

Bootees

Materials : $\frac{3}{4}$ oz. 3-ply baby wool in white, one pair
of No. 10 knitting-needles.

Measurements : $4\frac{1}{4}$ ins. deep, length of foot, 4 ins.

Tension : 8 sts. and 10 rows to 1 in.

Cast on 44 sts. and work in patt. as follows : *1st row :*
(P. 2, k. 4, p. 1) 6 times, p. 2.   *2nd row :* (K. 2, p. 1, k. 1,
p. 3) 6 times, k. 2.   *3rd row :* (P. 2, k. 2, p. 1, k. 2)
6 times, p. 2.   *4th row :* (K. 2, p. 3, k. 1, p. 1) 6 times,
k. 2.   *5th row :* (P. 3, k. 4) 6 times, p. 2.   *6th row :* As
4th.   *7th row :* As 3rd.   *8th row :* As 2nd.   These 8 rows
form the patt.   Rep. them twice.   *Next row :* (K. 2,
k. 2 tog., m. 1) to last 2 sts., k. 2.   K. back.   *Next row :*
K. 28, turn.   *Next row :* K. 14, turn.   Work 17 rows
on these 14 sts.   Now. with r.s. of work facing, beg.

where sts. were left and using same needle with 14 sts. on it, k. up 14 sts. evenly along side of instep, k. 14 across sts. on needle, k. up 14 sts. along second side of instep, k. last 14 sts. (70 sts.). K. 13 rows.

Shape foot : *1st row :* K. 1, k. 2 tog., k. 30 (k. 2 tog.) twice, k. 30, k. 2 tog., k. 1. *2nd row :* K. 31 (k. 2 tog.) twice, k. 31. *3rd row :* K. 1, k. 2 tog., k. 27 (k. 2 tog.) twice, k. 27, k. 2 tog., k. 1. *4th row :* K. 28 (k. 2 tog.) twice, k. 28. *5th row :* K. 27 (k. 2 tog.) twice, k. 27. Cast off.

Knit a second bootee to match.

To make up : Press gently. Join seam. Crochet thread 14 ins. long and draw through ankle holes. Attach small tassels to ends.

Romper

Materials : 3 oz. 3-ply non-shrink wool ; a pair each of Nos. 10 and 11 knitting-needles ; 6 small buttons,

Measurements : Length from shoulder to crutch. 16 or 17 ins.

Tension : 8 sts. to 1 in. over pattern.

Special Abbreviations : W.o. = wool over needle purlwise, *i.e.*, over needle towards you and then under needle away from you. P.w.o. 3 = lift loop thus formed over the next 3 plain sts.

Notes : The romper is knitted in one piece, starting at lower back. The pattern consists of one row, alternating with 3 rows of st. st.

Back : Using No. 10 needles, cast on 25 sts. for wrapover between legs. Work 10 rows m. st., then cast on 30 sts. and work in m. st. across these 30 sts. and the original 25 ; cast on 30 sts., then m. st. 35, k. 16, m. st. 34.

Next row : M. st. 34, p. 16, m. st. 35.

Now begin patt. as follows :

1st row : M. st. 35, *w.o., k. 3, p.w.o. 3, k. 3, rep. from * twice, k. 1, m. st. to end of row.

2nd row : M. st. 34, p. 16, m. st. 35.

3rd row : M. st. 35, k. 16, m. st. 34.

4th row : As 2nd row.

5th row : M. st. 35, k. 3, *w.o., k. 3, p.w.o. 3, k. 3, rep. from * once, k. 4, m. st. 10, turn ; sl. 1, p. 40, turn ; sl. 1, k. 40, m. st. 10, turn ; sl. 1, p. 60, turn ; *w.o., k. 3, p.w.o. 3, k. 3, rep. from * to last 8 sts., turn ; sl. 1, p. to end.

6th row : K. to last 8 sts., m. st. 8.

7th row : P.

8th row : Patt. across whole row, as follows : k. 2, *w.o., k. 3, p.w.o. 3, k. 3, rep. from * to end, ending with k. 2.

9th row : P. *10th row :* K. *11th row :* P.

12th row : Patt. whole row, but begin with k. 5, not k. 2.

13th, 14th and 15th rows : As 9th, 10th and 11th rows.

Cont. in patt. until 19 patts. have been worked and work measures $8\frac{1}{2}$ ins. at side, including m. st. border (21 patts. and $9\frac{1}{2}$ ins. for larger size) ; finish with a p. row.

Shape for Waist : Change to No. 11 needles and dec.

all along row as follows : k. 1, *k. 2 tog., k. 7, rep. from *, ending k. 2 tog., k. 1. (75 sts.). Work 10 rows in k. 1, p. 1 rib, then p. 1 row.

Now, with right side of work facing, begin patt. again with No. 10 needles, and work until 3rd patt. has has been completed, ending with a p. row.

Sleeves and Yoke : Cast on 21 sts.

M. st. 6 (beg. k. 1) to make a border, k. across remaining 15 of the cast-on sts., k. 35 of the back sts., m. st. 6, then transfer remaining sts. to a spare needle, and turn. Cont. in patt. on this half of yoke for 2 patts., keeping the borders of 6 m. st. at each end of needle.

Now make a buttonhole in centre of neck opening border as follows : m. st. 3, cast off 1, m. st. 1 ; on the next row work m. st. 2, cast on 2, m. st. 2.

Cont. in patt. for 3 more patts., then make another buttonhole as before.

Cont. for 2 more patts., ending with a k. row, then begin m. st. neck border. M. st. 20, p. to last 6 sts., m. st. 6. Work 3 more rows, and in the third of these make another buttonhole. Cont. until m. st. border is 8 rows deep, finishing with a k. row.

Cast off 14 sts. at beg. of next row (at neck edge), m. st. 6 and work to end of row. Cont. in patt. for 3 more patts. (12 rows) for shoulder, then leave these sts. on a spare needle, and return to sts. for other half of yoke.

Cast on 7 sts. for button flap. M. st. 6 (beg. k. 1), then k. to end of row. At beg. of next row cast on 21 sts. for left sleeve.

Cont. in patt. to match right yoke and sleeve, finishing

Plate XVII

CLOTHES FOR THE SECOND YEAR

After his first birthday baby will begin to discard layette stage garments. When "on show," little girls will wear a dress, and little boys a romper suit, or a smocked tunic or jersey, with a pilch. Most of the time, however, they will both be happy in practical dungarees, worn with a blouse, T-shirt or jersey, according to temperature. For cold weather the twin set shown above will be cosy and neat—see page 252 for instructions. The following pages show a dress and panties set, which can be adapted to make a boy's romper suit, a blouse and dungarees, which can be modified to make a short-legged sunsuit or pants with braces. Directions for making all these are given on pages 213–222.

Once baby begi
to crawl, he —
she—will nee
something to pr
tect both knees ar
clothing.   Room
dungarees are pro
ably the best answe
Make them i
strong denim
something simila
in a bright but n
pale colour.   T
little blouse is sui
able for either bo
or girl; in winter
can be replaced
a jersey — see t
one in Plate XV

Plate XVIII

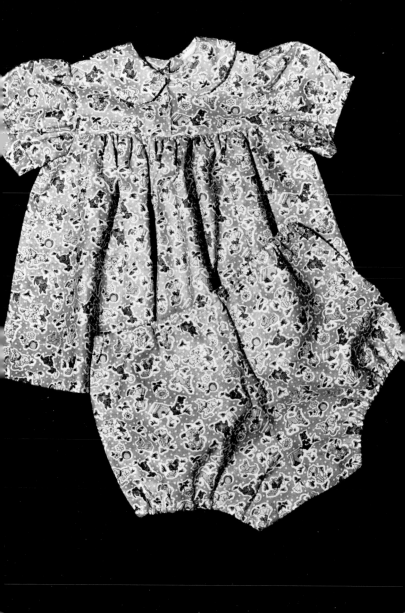

Plate XIX

Dress and Panties for a Little Girl

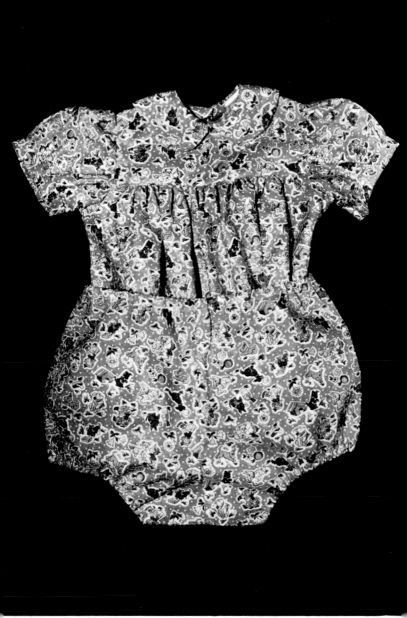

Romper Suit for Boy adapted from Dress and Panties

the shoulder with a p. row and the 6 m. st. border. At beg. of next row cast on 30 sts. (for front of neck) ; knit up the right shoulder sts., keeping the neck and sleeve m. st. borders.

Cont. in patt. for 8 rows, keeping 42 sts. in m. st. for neck border and 6 sts. in m. st. at either end for sleeve borders. On the final k. row, k. 2 tog. at one corner only of yoke, to obtain correct number of sts. Now work right across in patt., keeping only the sleeve borders in m. st., until 6 patts. have been worked after neck border.

At beg. of next rows cast off the 21 sleeve sts. Work 3 more patts., ending with a p. row.

Shape for Waist : Change to No. 11 needles and work 10 rows in k. 1, p. 1 rib, then change back to No. 10 needles and cont. in patt. for 19 patts. (21 patts. for larger size).

After last patt. row, p. to last 8 sts., turn ; sl. 1, k. 64, turn ; sl. 1, p. 54, turn ; sl. 1, k. 44 in patt., turn ; sl. 1, p. 34, turn ; sl. 1, k. 24, turn ; sl. 1, p. to end.

Next row : M. st. 32, patt. 16, m. st. 33. Work 7 more rows, keeping centre 16 sts. in patt. and leg borders in m. st.

Cast off 29 sts. at beg. of next 2 rows, and work the rem. 25 sts. in m. st. for wrap between legs. Work 8 rows.

On next 2 rows make 3 buttonholes as for neck opening, then work 2 rows m. st., and cast off.

To make up : Sew up side seams. Sew the bottom of the m. st. button flap at neck opening to bottom of

m. st. buttonhole border ; sew on all buttons. Press lightly under a damp cloth.

Pilch

Materials : 2 oz. 3-ply baby wool in white, one pair each of Nos. 10 and 12 knitting-needles.

Measurements : 22 ins. round widest part, 8 ins. from crutch to front, 9 ins. from crutch to back.

Tension : 8 sts. and 10 rows to 1 in. in ribbing on No. 10 needles.

Cast on 82 sts. on No. 12 needles and rib $\frac{1}{2}$ in. *Next row :* (K. 1, p. 1, k. 2 tog., m. 1) to last 2 sts., k. 1, p. 1. Cont. in rib for a further $\frac{1}{2}$ in. *Next row :* (K. 2, k. twice into next st., k. 1) 20 times, k. 2 (102 sts.). *Next row :* K. Change to No. 10 needles. Rib 54 rows. Now work as follows : *1st row :* Rib to last 6 sts., turn. *2nd row :* Rib to last 6 sts., turn. *3rd and 4th rows :* Rib to last 12 sts., turn. Work in this way, working 6 less sts. on every row until 30 sts. rem. in centre (12 rows), turn and rib to end. Now cast off 36 sts. loosely in rib and work to end. *Next row :* Cast off 36 sts. loosely in rib and work to end, cast on 36 sts. loosely. *Next row :* Rib to end and cast on 36 sts. loosely. *Next 2 rows :* Rib to last 36 sts., turn. *Next 2 rows :* Rib to last 30 sts., turn. Cont. in this way, working 6 sts. more on every row until all sts. are again on needle. Work 54 rows. *Next 2 rows :* Rib to last 8 sts., turn. *Next 2 rows :* Rib to last 16 sts., turn. Cont. in this way until 22 sts. remain in centre, turn and rib to end. Change to

No. 12 needles. *Next row :* K. *Next row :* (K. 2, k. 2 tog., k. 1) 20 times, k. 2 (82 sts.). Rib ½ in. *Next row :* (K. 1, p. 1, k. 2 tog., m. 1) to last 2 sts., k. 1, p. 1. Rib a further ½ in. Cast off.

To make up : Pick up 78 sts. round leg and k. 2 rows. Rib ½ in. Cast off in rib. Work other leg to match. Join side seams. Make a crochet cord 24 ins. long and thread through holes. Attach 2 small tassels to ends.

First-size Cardigan

Materials : 2 oz. 3-ply baby wool, 6 buttons, one pair each of Nos. 10 and 12 knitting-needles.

Measurements : Length, 11 ins. ; chest, 20 ins. ; sleeve seam, 6 ins.

Tension : 8 sts. and 10 rows to 1 **in.** in patt. on No. 10 needles.

Back : With No. 12 needles, cast on 80 sts. and work in rib of k. 1, p. 1 for 16 rows, taking last 2 sts. of last row tog. Change to No. 10 needles and patt. and work as follows : *1st row :* (P. 2, k. 4, p. 1) 11 times, p. 2. *2nd row :* (K. 2, p. 1, k. 1, p. 3) 11 times, k. 2. *3rd row :* (P. 2, k. 2, p. 1, k. 2) 11 times, p. 2. *4th row :* (K. 2, p. 3, k. 1, p. 1) 11 times, k. 2. *5th row :* (P. 3, k. 4) 11 times, p. 2. *6th row :* As 4th. *7th row :* As 3rd. *8th row :* As 2nd. These 8 rows complete the patt. and are rep. throughout. Cont. until work measures 6½ ins. from beg. To shape arm-holes, cast off 3 sts. at beg. of next 2 rows, then take 2 tog. at each end of next 23 k. rows. Cast off rem. 27 sts.

Right Front : With No. 12 needles, cast on 45 sts. and work as follows : *1st row :* K. 7 (k. 1, p. 1) 19 times. *2nd row :* (K. 1, p. 1) 19 times, k. 7. Rep. these 2 rows 7 times, working a buttonhole (k. 2, k. 2 tog., m. 1, k. 3) on the 8th row of the border (r.s. facing). Work a buttonhole on every 18th row thereafter, 6 buttonholes in all. Change to No. 10 needles and work as follows : K. 7, patt. to end, taking last 2 sts. together. Cont. in patt., always working 7 sts. at centre edge in k. for border. When work measures 6½ ins., shape arm-holes. Cast off 3 sts. at arm-hole edge at beg. of next w.s. row, then take 2 tog. at arm-hole edge at end of next 12 r.s. rows. On next r.s. row k. 7 and put on safety-pin, work to end of row, taking last 2 sts. tog. Cont. to dec. at arm-hole edge in usual way, and also take 2 tog. at neck edge at end of next 11 rows. Pull last stitch through.

Left Front : Work to match right front, reversing all shapings and omitting buttonholes.

Sleeve : With No. 12 needles, cast on 40 sts. and rib for 16 rows. *Next row :* K. 3 (k. twice into next st., k. 1) 18 times, k. 1 (58 sts.). Change to No. 10 needles and patt., and cont. until work measures 6 ins. Shape top of sleeve. Cast off 3 sts. at beg. of next 2 rows, then take 2 tog. at both ends of next 23 r.s. rows. Cast off rem. 6 sts.

To make up : Press all pieces lightly under damp cloth. Join sleeves to body. Pick up 7 sts. from safety-pin on right front, 16 sts. from front, 6 sts. from top of right sleeve, 25 sts. from back, 6 sts. from top of left sleeve, 16 sts. from left front and 7 sts. from safety-pin

IMPORTANT STEPS TO BABY'S WELL-BEING

Delicious
OVALTINE
Helps Mothers to Breast-feed their Babies

Breast-milk is naturally constituted to suit baby's delicate digestion and to provide nutritive elements for healthy growth.

Experience proves the value of 'Ovaltine' to expectant and nursing mothers. Doctors and nurses recommend that it be taken regularly before and after baby comes, to help in stimulating an ample supply of breast-milk. 'Ovaltine' also assists in maintaining the mother's strength while nursing.

OVALTINE
Chuckles
BABY'S FIRST SOLID FOOD

'Ovaltine' Chuckles make the ideal first solid food for babies. They fortify the usual milk diet with minerals and additional vitamins B and D. Deliciously crisp and sweet, 'Ovaltine' Chuckles can be easily powdered for mixing with milk to provide a nourishing and economical weaning food.

OVALTINE RUSKS
A Comfort to Baby at Teething-time

From teething-time onwards give baby 'Ovaltine' Rusks to bite and chew. They help to bring teeth easily and comfortably through the gums. This natural biting exercise also assists in keeping the teeth sound and regularly spaced, and in promoting the correct formation of the mouth. Made from the finest ingredients, 'Ovaltine' Rusks are nourishing, delicious and easy to digest.

on left front (83 sts.). Work 6 rows garter st. Cast off. Join sleeve and side seams, sew on buttons, neaten buttonholes.

Pram Coat

Materials : 4 oz. 4-ply fingering in white, a small quantity of blue, one pair of No. 10 knitting-needles, 3 buttons.

Measurements : Length, 13 ins. ; chest, 21 ins. ; under-arm seam, 6 ins.

Tension : 7 sts. and 10 rows to 1 in. in patt.

Back : Cast on 92 sts. in blue and k. 4 rows. Change to white and k. 4 rows. Rep. these 8 rows once. Rep. first 4 rows. These 20 rows form blue and white border. Now change to white and work in patt. as follows :
1st row : K. 2nd row : (K. 1, p. 3) to end of row. 3rd row : K. 4th row : P. 2, *k. 1, p. 3 *, rep. from * to * until last 2 sts., k. 1, p. 1.

These 4 rows complete the patt. and are rep. throughout.

Cont. until work measures 8 ins., ending on a w.s. row. Work 8 rows in patt. in blue, decreasing on first of these rows as follows : *K. 2, k. 2 tog., k. 3, k. 2 tog. Rep. from * to last 2 sts., k. 2 (72 sts.). Change to white and work 8 rows in patt. Cast off 2 sts. at beg. of next 2 rows for arm-holes. Now shape for raglan shoulder by taking 2 sts. tog. at both ends of next 19 k. rows (30 sts.). Cast off.

Right Front : Cast on 43 sts., and work 20 rows, border as for back. Change to white and work as

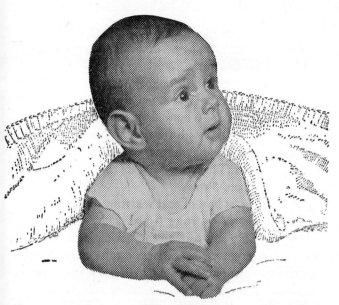

Soothe Baby's Colic

Colic pains are most distressing for babies. No wonder they cry for 'Milk of Magnesia'. Soothing, tasteless and comforting—it shifts the wind, relieves the colic and keeps baby regular and comfortable inside. For baby's sake (and yours!) keep 'Milk of Magnesia' handy.

'MILK of MAGNESIA' REGD.

SO SURE—SO SAFE—SO GENTLE

follows : *1st row :* K. *2nd row :* Patt. 36, k. 7. *3rd row :* K. *4th row :* Patt. 36, k. 7. Cont. until work measures 8 ins., and matches back. Work 8 rows in patt. in blue, decreasing on first of these rows as follows : K. 7, *k. 2 tog., k. 3, k. 2 tog., k. 2, rep. from * to end of row (35 sts.), and working a buttonhole (k. 3, k. 2 tog., m. 1, k. 1, patt. to end), on 5th row of this blue waist-band, and again on 21st and 37th rows of bodice.

After 8 rows of blue waist-band are completed, change to white and patt. 8 rows.

Cast off 2 sts. at beg. of next w.s. row, then take 2 tog. at end of next 14 r.s. rows (19 sts.). *Next row :* R.s. facing, cast off 7 sts., patt. to end, taking last 2 sts. tog. Take 2 tog. at neck edge on next 6 rows and arm-hole edge on r.s. rows only and cont. to dec. at arm-hole edge on next 2 r.s. rows. Cast off.

Left Front : Work to match right front, reversing all shapings and omitting buttonholes.

Sleeves (both alike) : Cast on 31 sts. and work border in blue to match body of work. Change to white and * k. twice into next 2 sts., k. 1. Rep. from * 10 times, k. twice into next st. (52 sts.). Now work in patt. in white until work measures 6 ins. from beg. Cast off 2 sts. at beg. of next 2 rows. Now take 2 tog. at each end of next 19 k. rows. Cast off rem. 10 sts.

Collar : Cast on 14 sts. in blue and work 4 rows garter st. Change to white and k. 11, k. last 3 sts. in blue, twisting wools at join. *Next row :* K. 3 blue, 11 white. Cont. in this way until collar measures $10\frac{1}{4}$ ins. then work 4 rows in blue. Cast off.

Everything for Baby

From nappies to outerwear . . .
from toys to playwear

Naturally, when you think of Harringtons you think of Harringtons famous nappies—but Harringtons are famous, too, for the best of everything in baby goods.

Here is a selection of the wide range of fine baby goods that Harringtons can offer:—

Harringtons Gauze Squares, Terry Squares, "Snapikins" (snap-fast nappy pants), Nursery Cotton Wool, Bath Towels, Face Towels and Face Cloths, Bibs, Feeders, Underwear, Outerwear, Frocks in Nylon and Tricel, Shorts, Playsuits, Rompers, Cot Sheets, Blankets, Mattress Covers, Pillow Cases, Quilts and Pram Rugs, Toys, Kot-Kid Safety Harnesses, Baby Soap, Baby Powder and the very latest in nappies— Harringtons "T" Shaped gauze nappy with a 12-fold protection pad.

Available from all good baby linen shops and departments.

Harringtons
Famous for Baby Goods

Look for the attractive blue and white packs and labels.

Harringtons baby goods have the recommendation of countless doctors and nurses, and the honour of being represented in the Royal Nurseries.

Send for your copy of Harringtons booklet "The Best for Baby," FREE.

HARRINGTONS (LONDON) LTD., NEW ADDINGTON, CROYDON, SURREY.

B.B.—16

To make up : Press all pieces under damp cloth. Join sleeves to body. Join seams. Sew collar to neck. Sew on buttons and neaten buttonholes. Press seams.

Leggings

Materials : 4 oz. 4-ply fingering in white and a small quantity in blue, one pair of No. 10 knitting-needles, elastic for waist.

Measurements : Waist to ankle, $14\frac{1}{2}$ ins. ; width at widest part, 26 ins.

Tension : 7 sts. and 10 rows to 1 in. in st. st.

Right Half of Leggings : Cast on 84 sts. Work 4 rows in k. 1, p. 1 rib. *5th row :* (K. 1, p. 1, m. 1, k. 2 tog.) 21 times. Work 8 rows in rib. *14th row :* K. 8, turn, p. back. *16th row :* K. 14, turn, p. back. *18th row :* K. 20, turn, p. back. Cont. in st. st., knitting 6 more sts. on each row, till 44 sts. have been worked, turn, p. back. *26th row :* K. 54, turn, p. back. *28th row :* K. twice in 1st st., k. to end.

Work in st. st., increasing at shaped end every 4th row, 6 times. Cont. on these 91 sts. till the straight edge measures $8\frac{1}{2}$ ins., finishing with a p. row.

To shape the Leg : K. 2 tog. at the beg. and end of next and every other row, till there are 50 sts. Work in st. st. for 2 ins. (or longer if desired), finishing with a p. row. *Next row :* (K. 2, m. 1, k. 2 tog.) in blue 12 times, k. 2. Work 3 rows in st. st. in blue. *4th row :* K. 36, turn, p. 22, turn. Work on these 22 sts. for $2\frac{1}{2}$ ins.

Break wool. Join wool at end of 14 sts. on right-hand needle (r.s. of work facing) and pick up and k. 17 sts. from right side of centre panel, k. 22 sts. on needle ; pick up and k. 17 sts. from left side of centre, k. 14 (84 sts.). *Next row :* P. *2nd row :* K. 5, turn, p. back. *4th row :* K. 8, turn, p. back. *6th row :* K. 11, turn, p. back. *8th row :* K. 14, turn, p. back. *10th row :* K. 16, k. 2 tog., k. 16, k. 2 tog., k. 12, k. 2 tog., k. 16, k. 2 tog., k. 16 (80 sts.). *11th row :* P. 5, turn, k. back. *13th row :* P. 8, turn, k. back. *15th row :* P. 11, turn, k. back. *17th row :* P. 14, turn, k. back. *19th row :* P. *20th row :* K. 2, k. 2 tog., k. 10, k. 2 tog., k. 16, k. 2 tog., k. 12, k. 2 tog., k. 16, k. 2 tog., k. 10, k. 2 tog., k. 2 (74 sts.). *21st row :* P. *22nd row :* K. 2, k. 2 tog., k. 26, k. 2 tog., k. 10, k. 2 tog., k. 26, k. 2 tog., k. 2 (70 sts.). *23rd row :* P. 2, p. 2 tog., p. to last 4 sts., p. 2 tog., p. 2 (68 sts.). *24th row :* K. 2, k. 2 tog., k. 24, k. 2 tog., k. 8, k. 2 tog., k. 24, k. 2 tog., k. 2 (64 sts.). *25th row :* As 23rd row (62 sts.). *26th row :* K. 2, k. 2 tog., k. to last 4 sts., k. 2 tog., k. 2 (60 sts.). *27th row :* As 23rd row (58 sts.). Cast off.

Left Half of Leggings : Work as for right half till the ribbing is finished.

15th row : K. *16th row :* P. 10, turn, k. back. *18th row :* P. 18, turn, k. back. Cont. as for right front half, reversing shaping and increasings.

To make up : Press lightly. Sew back and front seams, then join leg seams. Thread elastic through holes at waist. Crochet a chain with 2 strands of wool, thread through holes at ankles, sew small tassels at ends.

Pastorale

by Wilson

Mitts

Materials : $\frac{1}{2}$ oz. 3-ply baby wool in white and a small quantity in blue, one pair each of Nos. 9 and 11 knitting-needles.

Measurements : Length, 5 ins., and 5 ins. in circumference.

Tension : $7\frac{1}{2}$ sts. and $9\frac{1}{2}$ rows to 1 in. on No. 9 needles.

With No. 11 needles, cast on 42 sts. and rib 4 rows in blue. Change to white and k. 1 row. Now cont. in rib in white until work measures 2 ins. from beg. *Next row :* K. 2 tog., m. 1 to last 2 sts., k. 2. Change to No. 9 needles and work 20 rows in patt. as for pram coat.

Shape top. *1st row :* (K. 1, k. 2 tog. t.b.l., k. 15, k. 2 tog., k. 1) twice. *2nd row :* P. *3rd row :* (K. 1, k. 2 tog. t.b.l., k. 13, k. 2 tog., k. 1) twice. *4th row :* P. *5th row :* (K. 1, k. 2 tog. t.b.l., k. 11, k. 2 tog., k. 1) twice. *6th row :* P. *7th row :* (K. 1, k. 2 tog. t.b.l., k. 9, k. 2 tog., k. 1) twice. *8th row :* P. Cast off.

To make up : Press under damp cloth. Join side seam. Make crochet cord 13 ins. long and thread through holes. Sew small tassel to each end.

Bonnet

Materials : $\frac{1}{2}$ oz. 3-ply baby wool in white and a small quantity in blue, one pair of No. 10 knitting-needles, ribbon.

Measurements : Width all round front edge, 11 ins.

Tension : $7\frac{1}{2}$ sts. and 10 rows to 1 in. in patt.

We're discovered the

MAGIC CARPET

IT'S a well-padded carpet-cum-mattress that fits inside the playpen—protecting baby from draughty floors, damp grass or any unfriendly surface. Magic Carpet always keeps in place (baby *cannot* move the playpen) and provides real protection for carpets. In clean-at-a-wipe bubbly plastic with gay nursery design. All this for less than £2! Two sizes: 48″ × 36″ and 39″ × 36″.

Discover the Magic Carpet for yourself—it's at your Nursery Shop.
If in difficulty write to the makers—Dept. 10.

SIMPLANTEX LIMITED · EASTBOURNE

Cast on 89 sts. in blue and work blue and white border as for pram coat. Change to white and work in rib (k. 1, p. 1) for 12 rows. Now work 24 rows in patt. as for coat, but working 1 p. row first, to reverse fabric when brim is turned up.

Now shape crown. *1st row :* (K. 9, k. 2 tog.) 8 times, k. 1. *2nd row and all alt. rows :* K. *3rd row :* (K. 8, k. 2 tog.) 8 times, k. 1. *5th row :* (K. 7, k. 2 tog.) 8 times, k. 1. *7th row :* (K. 6, k. 2 tog.) 8 times, k. 1. *9th row :* (K. 5, k. 2 tog.) 8 times, k. 1. *11th row :* (K. 4, k. 2 tog.) 8 times, k. 1. *13th row :* (K. 3, k. 2 tog.) 8 times, k. 1. *15th row :* (K. 2, k. 2 tog.) 8 times, k. 1. *17th row :* (K. 1, k. 2 tog.) 8 times, k. 1. *19th row :* (K. 2 tog.) 8 times, k. 1. Break off wool, run thread through rem. sts. and fasten off securely.

To make up : Press under damp cloth. Join seam from centre of crown to ½ in. below crown shaping. Press seam. Turn back border. Make small rosettes of ribbon and attach to bonnet, leaving long enough ends to tie.

Boy's Cap

Materials : ½ oz. 3-ply baby wool in white and a small quantity of blue, one pair of No. 10 knitting-needles.

Measurements : Width round lower edge, 14 ins.

Tension : 7½ sts. and 10 rows to 1 in. as for bonnet.

Cast on 111 sts. in blue and work blue and white border as for pram coat. Change to white wool and rib 12 rows. Now change to patt. and work 16 rows,

Every mother's ambition

Every mother wants a *KAMELLA* BABY BAG . . . to keep her baby happy and healthy—safe from the COMMON COLD by day and night. In soft, non-irritating pure wool (or wool and nylon) with easily sterilized waterproof sheet and rubber buttons. Washable and hard-wearing; used and approved by leading Nursery Training Colleges and in several Royal Nurseries. FULLY GUARANTEED—replaced willingly if proved faulty in wash or wear. In several dainty colours from about 52/6.

Kamella

The original BABY BAG

Also the Bag/Dressing Gown, Dressing Gowns, Pram Coats and Sets, Duffle Coats, Pixie Suits, Rugs, Blankets and Underwear etc. At all good Stores and Baby Shops. Kamella Ltd., Bolton Road, Bradford.

Write for FREE illustrated catalogue.

One of the Kamella **GUARANTEED** Health Garments

working 1 p. row first, to reverse fabric when brim is turned up. Shape crown as follows : 1st row in blue : (K. 9, k. 2 tog.) 10 times, k. 1. All alt. rows K. 3rd row in blue : (K. 8, k. 2 tog.) 10 times, k. 1. 5th row in white : (K. 7, k. 2 tog.) 10 times, k. 1. 7th row in white : (K. 6, k. 2 tog.) 10 times, k. 1. 9th row in blue : (K. 5, k. 2 tog.) 10 times, k. 1. 11th row in blue : (K. 4, k. 2 tog.) 10 times, k. 1. 13th row in white : (K. 3, k. 2 tog.) 10 times, k. 1. 15th row in white : (K. 2, k. 2 tog.) 10 times, k. 1. 17th row in blue : (K. 1, k. 2 tog.) 10 times, k. 1. 19th row in blue : K. 2 tog. 10 times, k. 1. Break off wool, draw thread through rem. sts. and fasten off securely.

Ear-pieces : Cast on 17 sts. in white and work in garter st. for 8 rows. Take 2 tog. at both ends of next 4 rows. *Next row :* K. 1, k. 2 tog., k. 3 tog., k. 2 tog., k. 1. *Next row :* K. 2 tog., k. 1, k. 2 tog. Pull thread through rem. sts. and fasten securely. Work second piece to match.

To make up : Press under damp cloth. Join back seam, taking care to reverse seam for turn-up border. Sew ear-pieces under sides of cap. Make 2 crochet cords 12 ins. long, sew small tassels to ends and attach to ends of ear-pieces.

Knitting for the Older Baby

During baby's second year, the most rewarding garments to knit are probably jerseys and cardigans, so we give overleaf a pattern for a quickly made twin set.

She's Farley Fed!

So frequently when you see a healthy, happy, bonny baby growing into contented childhood you will hear Mother say, "She's Farley Fed," as though that were the complete answer.

It means, of course, that to Mother's loving care and attention has been added the wisdom of choosing Farley's Rusks when baby first starts on solids —because nearly all babies love their feed of Farley's and never seem to tire of them—they are so nourishing and sustaining, too.

Farley's is so easy to prepare—you just add the milk—no sugar is required. Give the older children Farley's and milk for breakfast—they love it!

You won't have any bother feeding Farley's.

FARLEYS RUSKS *— Baby's first solid food —*

Jersey and Cardigan

(See Plate XVII)

Materials : Of " Chieftain " pure Shetland wool (or a 4-ply knitting wool), 4 oz. for cardigan, 3 oz. for jersey (with long or short sleeves), 6 oz. for set ; 1 pair each Nos. 11 and 12 needles ; 4 buttons ; 3 press fasteners.

Measurements : Cardigan : Width all round under arms, 23 ins. ; length, $12\frac{1}{2}$ ins. ; sleeve seam, $8\frac{1}{2}$ ins. Jersey : width all round, 22 ins. ; length, 12 ins. ; sleeve seam, $2\frac{1}{2}$ or $8\frac{1}{2}$ ins.

Tension : 7 sts. and 9 rows = 1 inch.

Special Abbreviations : Twist 2 = put needle at back of work, k. 2nd st. on left-hand needle through *back* of st., then k. 1st st., and slip both sts. off needle ; R.s.f. = right side of work facing ; w.s.f. = wrong side facing ; k. 2 tog. B. = k. 2 tog. through *backs* of sts.

Jersey Front : With No. 12 needles, cast on 74 sts.

1st row : *K. 2, p. 2 ; rep. from * to last 2 sts., k.2.

2nd row : *P. 2, k. 2 ; rep. from * to last 2 sts., p. 2.

3rd row : *K. 2, p. 2, twist 2, p. 2 ; rep., from * to last 2 sts., k. 2.

4th row : As 2nd.

Rep. last 4 rows 3 times. Change to No. 11 needles.

17th row : K. 18, p. 2, k. 2, p. 2, k. 6 (inc. in next st., k. 4) 4 times, p. 2, k. 2, p. 2, k. 18 (78 sts.).

18th row : P. 18, k. 2, p. 2, k. 2, p. 30, k.2, p. 2, k. 2, p. 18.

Chilprufe

PURE | **WOOL** *for*

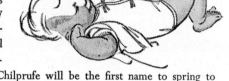

During the period when you are preparing the layette in happy expectancy, an important consideration will be your child's under-wear, and no doubt Chilprufe will be the first name to spring to your mind.

Chilprufe garments, especially for the Layette, have always been highly esteemed not only by mothers, but by the Medical and Nursery professions.

The soft knitted wool fabric is non-irritant to the most delicate skin and will retain its colour throughout repeated washings, whilst the beautiful workmanship and finish is greatly appreciated.

Wrapper Vests, Nightgowns, Sleeping Suits, Baby Petticoats, Baby Frocks, Baby Crawler Suits, Baby Cardigans, Pram Coats, Bonnets, Mittens and Socks, Soft Shoes.

Write direct for Children's Catalogue

CHILPRUFE MILLS · LEICESTER

19th row : K. 18, p. 2, twist 2, p. 2, k. 30, p. 2, twist 2, p. 2, k. 18.

Cont. in patt. until work measures 7½ ins. from beg.

Shape armholes : R.s.f., cast off 2 sts. at beg. of next 2 rows ; dec. at both ends of next 3 rows (68 sts.), then at both ends of alternate rows until 62 sts. remain★★★.

Next row : (W.s.f.), P. 10, k. 2, p. 2, k. 2 (p. 4, p. 2 tog.) 4 times, p. 6, k. 2, p. 2, k. 2, p. 10 (58 sts.)★.

Work in correct rib patt. for 2 ins.

Shape for neck : R.s.f., rib 24 sts., turn, finish this side first.

Dec. at neck edge on every row 4 times ; then on every other row twice (18 sts.). Work 3 rows. Cast off at armhole edge, 9 sts. twice.

Slip centre 10 sts. on to a safety pin.

R.s.f., join wool and work on last 24 sts. to match first side.

Jersey Back : Work as for front as far as★.

Start back opening : *1st row :* (K. 2, p. 2, twist 2, p. 2) 3 times, k. 6 ; turn work, finish this side first.

2nd row : K. 4 (p. 2, k. 2) 6 times, p. 2.

Work in rib patt., with 4 K. sts. at beg. of all P. rows, until armhole measures the same as on front, then cast off 9 sts. at beg. of next 2 k. rows ; put last 12 sts. on safety pin.

Join wool at centre, cast on 2 sts.

1st row : K. 6 (including the 2 cast-on sts.) (p. 2, twist 2, p. 2, k. 2) 3 times.

CHOOSE

Choodler

FOR BABY

Baby is a joy to see in Choodler Baby Pants — dainty, durable, hygienic — and snug, too, in Choodler nightwear in 'Osmalane', roomy and deep-hemmed. Also for baby's wardrobe are attractive Choodler petticoats.

Nylon and plastic, plain or lace trimmed.

Nylon lace, frilled locknit and plastic.

BV Plastic

Choodler day / night-gown, hand-embroidered, trimmed with nylon lace.

Nylon taffeta and locknit petticoats.

Nylon and plastic, plain or lace trimmed.

BV Plastic

TRADE MARK

WILLIAM H. STOREY & CO. LTD., COMBERTON, CAMBS

2nd row : (P. 2, k. 2) 6 times, p. 2, k.4. Finish off to match other side.

Jersey Neck Band : Stitch front to back at shoulders. Join wool at centre back, and, with r.s.f. and No. 12 needles, k. 6, p. 2, k. 2, p. 2 from sts. of back on safety pin ; pick up and k. 16 sts. around neck ; rib 10 sts. of centre front from safety pin ; pick up and k. 16 sts. to shoulder seam ; p. 2, k. 2, p. 2, k. 6 from back (66 sts.).

1st row : K. 4 (p. 2, k. 2) 14 times, p. 2, k. 4.

2nd row : K. 6 (p. 2, twist 2, p. 2, k. 2) 7 times, k. 4. Work 4 rows in rib patt. Cast off loosely in rib.

Jersey Sleeves : (Both alike) : Begin at the top and work downwards. (This allows for easy lengthening, as required.)

Short sleeves : With No. 11 needles, cast on 12 sts. Work in st. st., and inc. at both ends of 2nd and every row following until there are 34 sts. Inc. at beg. of every row until there are 50 sts.**.

Cast on 2 sts. at beg. of next 2 rows (54 sts.).

Dec. at both ends of every 4th row until there are 48 sts.****.

Change to No. 12 needles. *1st row:* R.s.f.: (K. 2, p. 2) 12 times. Work 8 rows in correct rib. Cast off.

Long Sleeves : Work up to ****, then dec. at both ends of every 6th row until 42 sts. remain. Work until sleeve edge measures 7 ins. (or length required). Change to No. 12 needles, and work 16 rows in rib patt. Cast off.

Maw's **Anticolic Teat**
the best—the most natural

Happy mother, happy babe! She chooses Maw's world-famous Anticolic Teat. "Cherry" shaped, supple yet firm. Maw's Teat ensures Baby's proper jaw development. Reversible for thorough cleaning, Maw's Anticolic Teats are available in three hole sizes. Individually plaquetted for absolute hygiene.

FROM CHEMISTS ONLY   PRICE 8d.

◄ **Maw's Dinky Feeder**

A unique miniature glass feeding bottle complete with Maw's Anticolic Teat. The ideal way of giving baby orange juice, medicine or a soothing drink. Maw's Brochure of Nursery Products gladly sent on receipt of a postcard.

Maw's—best for baby

S. MAW SON AND SONS LIMITED · BARNET · HERTS

B.B.—17

Cardigan Right Front: (Make buttonholes on this front, if cardigan is for a girl see Left Front for instructions.) With No. 12 needles, cast on 50 sts. Work 16 rows in patt., as for front of jersey, then start main part.

(Note : Work 8 rib sts. with No. 12 needles on *every* row. This achieves the correct length, does away with the need for sewing a border to cardigan, and makes a neater finish.)

1st row : Rib 8 sts., change to No. 11 needles, k. 18, p. 2, k. 2, p. 2, k. 18.

2nd row : P. 18, k. 2, p. 2, k. 2, p. 18. Change to No. 12 needles, rib. 8.

Work in patt. until work measures $7\frac{1}{2}$ ins. from beg. R.s.f., start front shaping.

1st row : Rib 8, k. 2 tog., patt. to end.

2nd row : Cast off 2, patt. to end.

3rd row : Rib 8, k. 2 tog., work to last 2 sts., k. 2 tog. (45 sts.).

4th row : P. 2 tog., patt. to end.

5th row : As 3rd row.

6th and 8th rows : P. to last 8 sts., rib 8.

7th row : Rib 8, work to last 2 sts., k. 2 tog. (41 sts.).

Rep. rows 5 to 8 twice (35 sts).

Work straight at armhole edge, and continue the front dec. after the 8 rib sts. on every 4th row until 26 sts. remain. Work 4 rows. Cast off 9 sts. at beg. of next 2 p. rows. Work in rib on 8 sts. for $1\frac{1}{4}$ ins. Cast off.

Cardigan Left Front Work as for right front for 7 rows.

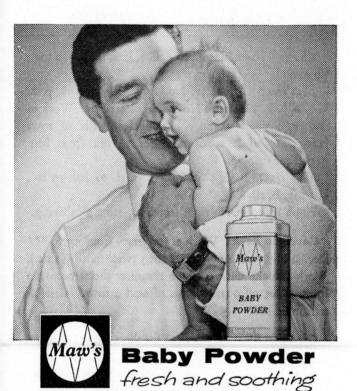

Maw's Baby Powder
fresh and soothing

Father and baby doing fine—with the cool, soothing touch of Maw's Baby Powder. This superfine, faintly perfumed powder contains Cetrimide—the gentle antiseptic for double protection. In blue-and-white sprinkler top tins.

FROM CHEMISTS ONLY. PRICE: 1/9
Family size economy tins. Price: **3/-**

Maw's Baby Cream ▶

A superfine antiseptic cream to soothe baby's skin, prevent nappie rash. Price: **2/9** *Maw's Brochure of Nursery Products gladly sent on receipt of a postcard.*

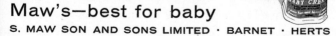

Maw's—best for baby
S. MAW SON AND SONS LIMITED · BARNET · HERTS

8th row : Make buttonhole: P. 2, k. 2, m. 1, p. 2 tog., rib to end.   Work 8 rows.

Next row : Change to. No. 11 needles ; k. 18, p. 2, k. 2, p. 2, k. 18 ; with No. 12 needles, rib 8.   Work in patt. and make 3 more buttonholes, with 18 rows between.   When work measures $7\frac{1}{2}$ ins. from beg. start front shaping.

Next row : R.s.f. ; cast off 2, patt. to last 10 sts., k. 2 tog. B, rib 8.

Finish off to match right front, reversing all shaping.

Cardigan Back : Work as for jersey front up to *★★★* Dec. at both ends of alternate rows twice more (58 sts.). Work straight until armhole measures the same as on front.   Cast off 9 sts. at beg. of next 4 tows.   Cast off remaining sts.

Cardigan Sleeve : Work as for short sleeves of jersey up to *★★*.   Inc. at beg. of next 6 rows (56 sts.).   Cast on 2 sts. at beg. of next 2 rows (60 sts.).   Dec. at both ends of every 4th row until there are 50 sts., then at both ends of every 6th row until 42 sts. remain.   Finish off as for long sleeves of jersey.

To make up : Press all parts (except ribbing) under a damp cloth with a hot iron ; press ribbing of yoke of jersey apart to correct width.

Join shoulder, side and sleeve seams, and sew in sleeves.   Join short ends of rib of cardigan, and sew this band across back neck.   Sew buttons on cardigan, and press fasteners on opening of jersey.   Give a final press.

Mummy's Precious!

Only a mother can savour the exquisite feeling of pride and joy mingled with awe which she feels as she holds her precious baby in her arms. The soft down on his head—which, of course, is going to curl—his eyes and chin just like Daddy's, those delicate fingers and perfect little toes! Her love is full to overflowing; nothing is too good for her baby. There is no sacrifice she will not willingly make to ensure that he has the best of everything.

A pity she cannot feed him herself, but she can and will give him the food that she knows will lay the foundation of good health for the years that lie ahead—Cow & Gate Milk Food. *Her* choice is made. Let it be yours too. Buy Cow & Gate for *your* baby today.

★ When baby weighs 15 lbs. see that he graduates to solids on Cow & Gate Cereal Food!

COW & GATE MILK FOOD

The FOOD *of* ROYAL BABIES

5690

Index

262

John's Brother's Wife told her

And she heard at the Clinic — that
by far the simplest way of ensuring baby
has a germ-free bottle for every feed
is to sterilise it with Milton. Otherwise his
tummy may get upset and then the smile
will depart ! So start following the
Milton Feeding Bottle Routine today.

Ask your chemist for a leaflet
Milton Antiseptic Ltd, 42-46 Weymouth St, London WI

Baby Luxury

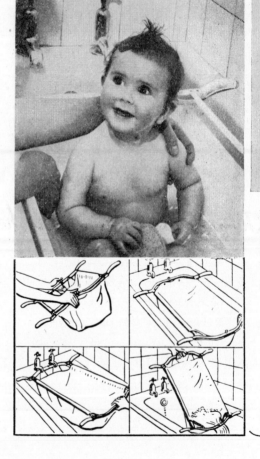

**POPPE
BABY**

Neat an...
mal bath...
water, s...
filled an...
All spl...
straight...
length 3...

"VENUS"

40″ body on New Continental type spring suspension chassis; 14″ tangent spoke wheels. Softly padded, washable plastic cloth upholstery; Marimo fabric hood and apron; push-on, pull-off brake.

2E TUBULAR HIGH CHAIR

De luxe high chair, strong, all tubular, enamel frame; with plastic quick-release tray and footrest; safety strap. Seat and backrest upholstered in soft, washable plastic cloth. Height 36″.

gree
Regd Trade Mark

ms

rsery Furniture

EVERYTHING FOR MOTHER AND HER BABY

Here at Treasure Cot you will find a full range of departments staffed by helpful, knowledgeable people — all possessed of an unerring skill in selecting the right clothes and equipment for mothers and their babies. Maternity, Layette, Furniture or Pram catalogues on request.